Nothing

Retold by Margaret Tarner

MACMILLAN

Founding Editor: John Milne

The Macmillan Readers provide a choice of enjoyable reading materials for learners of English. The series is published at six levels – Starter, Beginner, Elementary, Pre-intermediate, Intermediate and Upper.

Level Control
Information, structure and vocabulary are controlled to suit the students' ability at each level.

The number of words at each level:

Starter	about 300 basic words
Beginner	about 600 basic words
Elementary	about 1100 basic words
Pre-intermediate	about 1400 basic words
Intermediate	about 1600 basic words
Upper	about 2200 basic words

Vocabulary
Some difficult words and phrases in this book are important for understanding the story. Some of these words are explained in the story, some are shown in the pictures, and others are marked with a number like this: ...[3]. Phrases are marked with [P]. Words with a number are explained in the *Glossary* at the end of the book and phrases are explained on the *Useful Phrases* page.

Answer Keys
Answer Keys for the *Points for Understanding* and *Exercises* sections can be found at www.macmillanenglish.com/readers.

Audio Download
There is an audio download available to buy for this title. Visit www.macmillanenglish.com/readers for more information.

Contents

A Note About The Author

William Shakespeare was born in the year 1564 in Stratford-upon-Avon, a town about eighty miles north-west of London. His father, John Shakespeare, was a well-known businessman, but he was often in debt. So, although William had a good education at the local school, there was not enough money for him to go to university.

In 1582, when Shakespeare was only eighteen, he married a twenty-six-year-old woman called Ann Hathaway. They had a daughter six months later and then twins were born in 1585.

We know nothing about Shakespeare's life for the next few years. However, we do know that by about 1590, he was working in London as an actor. By 1592, Shakespeare was already well-known as a playwright. We know this because another playwright, Robert Greene, was jealous of Shakespeare's success. In 1592 Greene wrote about Shakespeare, saying that he was uneducated and making fun of Shakespeare's name.

Shakespeare soon started to write plays for a company of actors in London called The Lord Chamberlain's Men. From 1599, they acted in a fine new theatre called the Globe, but they were sometimes called to the royal court to put on a play for Queen Elizabeth I. All the plays were read by the Lord Chamberlain before they were performed. He had to make sure that nothing in the play would upset the Queen.

There were about 200,000 people living in London at this time and there were only four or five theatres for them to visit. These theatres were round or eight-sided buildings, and they held about 3000 people. The audience stood around three sides of the stage. There was no roof over the central part of the theatre so most people, including the actors, had no protection from the weather. Rich people paid more to sit down and be under cover.

At the back of the stage, there was a balcony for musicians and another for the actors to use. The space under the balconies was part of the stage, but could be separated from it by a curtain. Actors walked onto the main stage through two doors at the back and they were always very close to the audience. Plays had to take place in daylight and so they began at two o'clock in the afternoon and finished by five in the evening.

The people of London always wanted new plays and sometimes six different ones were performed by a company in one week. At that time plays were not often published, so a clever playwright could make old plays into new ones by writing extra scenes or changing parts of the story. Shakespeare sometimes took stories from other writers and sometimes he made them up. He knew the actors in the company well, so he was able to write parts that would suit them. He worked very fast and knew just what his audience wanted. His plays could frighten people, or make them laugh or cry and this is what made them so popular.

Shakespeare's name soon became well known. Some playwrights, like Greene, laughed at Shakespeare because he had never been to university. But others respected him and became his friends.

During his years in London, Shakespeare often went to Stratford to visit his family. By 1613 he had retired[1] and lived back in his home town, where he had bought a big house. He lived there until his death in 1616.

All the theatres where Shakespeare worked, including the Globe, were destroyed long ago. However, there is now a new Globe on the South Bank of the River Thames. There you can see Shakespeare's plays performed just as they were in his lifetime. It is an exciting experience.

A Note About This Play

Much Ado About Nothing was written and first acted towards the end of 1598. It was printed a year or so later and soon became very popular.

Shakespeare wrote many comedies – plays which are written to make the audience laugh – and *Much Ado About Nothing* is one of these. The play has a happy ending, and like all Shakespeare's comedies, it is also a love story. All of the action in the play takes place in the city of Messina, a port in the north-east of Sicily, which was then governed by Spain. The main story, or plot, is about two young lovers, Count Claudio and the rich and beautiful Hero, whose father is the Governor[2] of Messina. They love each other very much and plan to get married. Their story nearly ends very unhappily, and such a sad ending would have turned the comedy into a tragedy. The same romantic story can be found in several Italian and French books of the time and Shakespeare borrowed it for the plot of his play. However, Shakespeare added another plot, which made *Much Ado About Nothing* one of Shakespeare's cleverest comedies.

This second plot is also a love story, but it is certainly not romantic, because Beatrice and Benedick find it difficult to believe that they could ever love each other. They spend most of their time arguing cleverly and pointing out each others' faults. Neither of them likes the idea of getting married to anyone and certainly not to each other.

But it is this story that people always remember because Beatrice and Benedick are so witty[3]. At the end of the play, their friends trick them into falling in love with each other, so their story has a happy ending too.

Shakespeare's plays were acted by members of his company and he often wrote parts for certain actors, who were well known to their audiences. One of these actors was a man called Will Kemp, who always played funny characters. Audiences loved him, but Shakespeare was often angry with Kemp because he added words of his own. Kemp was the first actor to play the part of Dogberry, the silly old man who, by mistake, discovers the villain[4] – Don John. Don John is the bastard[5] brother of Don Pedro. This is an important part of the story because it means that the play can end happily.

Shakespeare wrote about a third of this play in a kind of poetry called *blank verse*. Blank verse does not rhyme, but each line has several strong beats, usually five. The romantic story of Claudio and Hero is told in blank verse and that makes it more sad and slow. Here is an example in Shakespeare's own words.

Claudio: O, my lord,
When **you** went **on**ward **on** this **en**ded **ac**tion,
I **looked** up**on** her **with** a **sol**dier's **eye**
That **liked**, but **had** a **rou**gher **task** in **hand**
Than **to** drive **lik**ing **to** the **name** of **love**.
But **now** I **am** re**turned**, and **that** war-**thoughts**
Have **left** their **pla**ces **va**cant, **in** their **rooms**
Come **throng**ing **soft** and **del**icate **de**sires,
All **promp**ting **me** how **fair** young **Hero** is …
Say**ing** I **liked** her **ere** I **went** to **wars**.

Shakespeare did not worry too much about the titles of his comedies. The title of this play means: A Lot of Trouble about Nothing – because Hero does nothing wrong. There is another meaning to the title – and it is a joke. The word 'nothing' was often spoken like 'noting' – listening to people in secret. Many of the problems in this play are caused by characters hearing things they do not understand or that are not true.

For more information about William Shakespeare, including projects and webquests, visit the Macmillan Readers website at www.macmillanenglish.com/readers.

This Version Of Much Ado About Nothing

This Macmillan Reader includes some 'real' extracts of text from *Much Ado About Nothing*. We hope that these texts will help readers to both understand and enjoy Shakespeare in the original. The extracts follow immediately after their simplified form. They are shaded in grey and have a separate glossary. In the glossary, words that are old English (no longer used in today's English) appear in *italics*. See the example (from page 11) below:

Beatrice: Then God help the worthy Claudio! Benedick is like a disease – easy to catch and difficult to get rid of. Now that Claudio has caught the Benedick disease, he'll have to spend all his money on medicine.

simplified text

Beatrice: *O lord, he will hang upon him like a disease: he is sooner caught than the pestilence, and the taker runs presently mad. God help the noble Claudio. If he have caught the Benedick, it will cost him a thousand pounds ere he be cured.*

original text

sooner = more quickly
pestilence = a serious illness which is easy to catch
runs = becomes
presently = at once
ere = before

glossary

The People In This Story

Don Pedro *Prince of Aragon, a kingdom in northern Spain*

Don John *brother of Don Pedro*

Leonato *Governor of Messina, in the north-east of Sicily*

Hero *Leonato's daughter*

Beatrice *Leonato's niece*

Claudio *a count[6] from Florence*

Benedick *a lord from Padua*

Borachio *Don John's friend*

Act 1, Scene 1

[Enter Leonato, who is the Governor of Messina, Hero, his daughter, and Beatrice, his niece, with a messenger who gives Leonato a letter]

Leonato: I see from this letter that the Spanish prince, Don Pedro, will soon be here in Messina.

Messenger: That's true. He is not far behind me.

Leonato: How many gentlemen were killed in this war?

Messenger: Few who were important and no one well known.

Leonato: That's good. It makes the victory[7] twice as welcome. I also read that Don Pedro of Aragon praises[8] a young man from Florence whose name is Claudio.

Messenger: That's right. Count Claudio deserves all the praise Don Pedro has given him. That young man behaved like an experienced soldier. I don't have the words to tell you how brave he was.

Leonato: Claudio's uncle is here in Messina. He will be very pleased to hear about his nephew's bravery.

Messenger: He already knows. He cried when he read about it, but his tears were happy ones.

Leonato: Those are the best kind of tears.

Beatrice: Excuse me, but has Signor Sharp-sword[9] returned from the war or not?

Messenger: Sharp-sword? There is no soldier with that name, lady.

Hero: My cousin means Signor Benedick of Padua.

Messenger: Oh, he's come back – still making jokes as usual.

Beatrice: Benedick's the man who challenged[10] Cupid, god of love, to a shooting match, here in Messina. My uncle's fool[11] said that he would shoot Cupid's arrows[12] for him, so that's two fools we are talking about! Signor Benedick is the bigger fool because he's sure that the little god's arrows will never reach his heart. *Do* tell me how many men Benedick killed in the war.

Messenger: Why do you want to know, lady?

Beatrice: Before he went away, I promised Signor Benedick that I would eat anyone he killed!

Leonato: You are very hard on Benedick, niece. But he'll have plenty to say to you, I am sure.

Messenger: He's a good soldier. He fought well, lady.

Beatrice: Well, he can fight a *lady*. He's brave enough for that. He's brave enough to eat bad food too. All soldiers have to. What a man! What a soldier!

Leonato: You must excuse my niece, sir. There is a merry[13] war of words between her and Signor Benedick. When they meet they always argue. They enjoy a challenge of wits[14].

Beatrice: And Benedick always loses at least four of his five wits in the challenge. Then he is no better than his own horse. Tell me, who is Benedick's best friend now? He changes his friends as often as he changes his hat. Then they both behave badly and are happy to go to the devil[15] together.

Messenger: Signor Benedick's close friend is now the noble[16] Claudio.

Beatrice: Then God help the noble Claudio! Benedick is like a disease – easy to catch and difficult to get rid of. Now that Claudio has caught the Benedick disease, he'll have to spend all his money on medicine.

> **Beatrice:** *O lord, he will hang upon him like a disease: he is sooner caught than the pestilence, and the taker runs presently mad. God help the noble Claudio. If he have caught the Benedick, it will cost him a thousand pounds ere he be cured.*
>
> sooner = more quickly
> *pestilence* = a serious illness which is easy to catch
> *runs* = becomes
> presently = at once
> *ere* = before

Leonato: That will never happen to you, niece.

Beatrice: No, not until we have summer in January.

Messenger: Here comes our prince, Don Pedro.

[Enter Don Pedro, Claudio, Benedick, Don John and Balthasar, who is a singer and servant of Don Pedro]

Don Pedro: Signor Leonato, I thank you for inviting us to stay. Our visit will give you a lot of trouble.

Leonato: No trouble at all. I am delighted to have you here.

Don Pedro: *[Smiling at Hero]* I think this must be your daughter.

Leonato: That's what her mother says and I believe her!

Benedick: And so you should, sir.

Leonato: Yes. You are too young to be her father!

Don Pedro: And she is just like you, Signor Leonato.

Benedick: Really? Does the daughter have her father's white hair?

[Don Pedro and Leonato walk away to talk together]

Beatrice: *[To Benedick]* Don't you ever stop talking? No one is listening to you.

Benedick: It's my Lady Scorn[17]! So you are still alive then.

Beatrice: Scorn feeds on the words of fools. Scorn will never go hungry when you are around.

Benedick: No other lady scorns me except you. All the others love me. It is a pity that I don't love them.

Beatrice: It's lucky for them that you don't. What an awful lover you would make! I am like you in one thing, though. I don't want loving words from anyone. I would rather hear my dog bark.

Benedick: I hope you never change your mind. Any lover of yours would be sure to have a scratched[18] face!

Beatrice: And that scratching would not make it worse than yours!

Benedick: You speak without sense, just like a parrot[19].

Beatrice: At least a parrot *can* speak. That makes the bird better than a *dumb*[20] animal, like a horse.

Don't you ever stop talking? No one is listening to you.

Benedick: Then I wish that my horse could move as fast as your tongue. And go so long without stopping! That's enough talk. I feel like stopping now.

Beatrice: Of course, you always want the last word.

Don Pedro: *[Who has been talking to Leonato]* That's all my news then.

[To Claudio and Benedick] Signor Claudio and Signor Benedick, my good friend Leonato has invited us all to stay for at least a month, maybe longer.

Leonato: You are all welcome. *[To Don John]* You too, sir, now that you are friends with your brother again.

Don John: I am a man of few words, but I thank you.

Leonato: *[To Don Pedro]* Please go first, sir.

Don Pedro: Let's go together.

[Exit everyone except Benedick and Claudio]

Claudio: Benedick, did you see Signor Leonato's daughter?

Benedick: I saw her, but I did not pay her any attention.

Claudio: Doesn't she look like a young girl worthy[21] of love?

Benedick: How do you want me to answer that? To give you the truth or mock[22] her as I mock all women?

Claudio: Tell me what you really think. I am serious.

Benedick: Well, she is too short for *high* praise. Her hair is too brown to call her *fair*[23] and she is too small for any *great* praise. I do not fancy[24] her at all.

Claudio: Please stop joking for a moment and tell me what you *really* think of Hero.

Benedick: Why, are you thinking of buying her?

Claudio: There is not enough money in the world to do that.

Benedick: I am beginning to think that you *are* serious.

Claudio: Hero is the sweetest lady I have ever seen.

Benedick: Surely not. Her cousin is far more beautiful – I can see that without wearing glasses. It's a pity that Lady Beatrice is so full of scorn and has such a sharp tongue. You don't want to *marry* Hero, do you?

> **Benedick:** *I can see yet without spectacles and I see no such matter. There's her cousin, an she were not possessed with a fury, exceeds her so much in beauty as the first of May doth the last of December. But I hope you have no intent to turn husband have you?*
>
> yet = still
> *an* = if
> possessed = controlled by
> fury = great anger
> *doth* = does
> intent = intention, plan

Claudio: With all my heart, I do.

Benedick: I can't believe it. Isn't every man afraid of having an unfaithful[25] wife? Will I never see a bachelor[26] of sixty? Are you happy to be caught and never to be free again? But here comes Don Pedro. He's looking for you, I think.

[Enter Don Pedro and Don John]

Don Pedro: Why did you not follow us? What secret have you two been discussing?

Benedick: If it's a secret, you must *order* me to tell you.

Don Pedro: Then I do. Tell me.

Benedick: You hear that, Count Claudio? I have to speak. Well, my friend Claudio is in love. Now you must ask with whom. To give you a short answer, Claudio is in love with Leonato's short daughter, Hero. And that's the truth, I'm sorry to say.

Claudio: I am *not* sorry and it's true. I love Hero and I always will.

Don Pedro: That's fine. The girl is worthy of your love.

Claudio: Do you really believe that, my lord?

Don Pedro: Yes, I do. That's what I really think.

Benedick: A woman worthy of love? That's something I shall never see.

15

Don Pedro: Well, we all know what you think about women.
Benedick: A woman gave birth to me and brought me up. I thank her for that. But no woman will ever make a fool of me. If I never marry, I shall never have to wear horns[27] – the sign of an unfaithful wife. By staying unmarried, I save money too. So, I will be a bachelor until I die.
Don Pedro: But before *I* die, I will see you pale with love!
Benedick: Pale with anger or illness, but not with love. I am not blind, like Cupid.
Don Pedro: But the little god will get you. No man escapes *his* arrows.
Benedick: Mock Benedick, the married man, not Benedick the bachelor. Cupid will never catch me.
Don Pedro: Don't be so sure. He has an arrow pointed at your heart.
Benedick: But it won't reach its target[28]!
Don Pedro: We'll see. Now, Signor Benedick, please go in to Leonato. Tell him I shall see him at dinner.
Claudio: Off you go, Signor Benedick – one day you'll be a married man, I'm sure of that.
Benedick: Don't mock me yet. I am going. *[Exit Benedick]*
Claudio: My lord, I would like you to help me.
Don Pedro: Of course. What can I do for you?
Claudio: Does Leonato have a son, my lord?
Don Pedro: Hero is his only child and heir[29]. Do you really love her, Claudio? Is that why you want my help?
Claudio: Oh, my dear lord, when I first went to fight,
I was thinking like a soldier.
I had seen Hero, but I did not love her.
War and brave actions were all I thought of.
But now I see fair Hero with new eyes.
New thoughts of love now fill my heart and mind.
Don Pedro: Your love for her will grow more every day.
Soon every word you say will be of love.

I'll speak to Hero and her father too.
You lucky man, the girl will soon be yours.
That's what you want, I know.
Claudio: Thank you, my lord. You understand me well.
I could say more – write a whole book of love!
Don Pedro: You've said enough. You are a man in love.
I have a plan. There will be dancing here tonight.
We'll all be wearing masks[30]. I can disguise[31] myself
So that fair Hero thinks that I am you.
I'll speak to her of love and win her heart.
Then I will tell her father everything
And straight away, that sweet girl will be yours.
[Exit]

Act 1, Scene 2

[Enter Leonato and his brother, Antonio]
Leonato: Has your son arranged the music for tonight?
Antonio: Don't worry, brother, it will all be ready. Now, I have something very strange to tell you.
Leonato: Is it good news or bad?
Antonio: Good, I think. This is what happened. Don Pedro and Claudio were walking in my garden, along a little path between some trees. Don Pedro was speaking very quietly – telling Claudio a secret, perhaps. So my servant[32] decided to listen. He heard Don Pedro say that he loved your daughter, Hero! He planned to tell her that evening at the dance. If Hero loved him, he would let you know at once.
Leonato: Are you sure? Did your servant really hear that?
Antonio: I'm sure he got it right, but I'll question him again.
Leonato: No, don't do that. Say nothing. But I'll talk to my daughter about it. Then she will know what to say. Tell her I want to see her.
[Enter servants. Leonato speaks to them] Friends, you all know what to do.
[To a musician] You, sir, come with me and we'll discuss the music. All of you get to work. We have lots to do.
[Exit]

Act 1, Scene 3

[Enter Don John and his friend, Conrad]

Conrad: What the devil's the matter, sir? Why are you looking so sad?

Don John: Everything makes me sad – there's no end to it.

Conrad: Why? You must have a reason for your feelings.

Don John: What difference would that make?

Conrad: You might find something to be happy about.

Don John: No clever talk will change *me*. It is my nature to be sad and I must always follow my own path. I do what I want, when I want to. I look after myself and care for no one.

Conrad: Yes, but you must hide your true feelings a little longer. You fought against your brother in the war, but he has forgiven you now. Make sure that you don't upset him. Please him, if you can.

Don John: I'd rather be a sharp thorn[33] to *hurt* my brother than be the sweet flower whose smell would *please* him. I have the bad blood of a bastard, you know that. Why should I try to be what I am not? I am an angry man and I don't try to hide it. I am like a bad dog who has to wear a muzzle[34] or a prisoner with a chain on his leg. If the muzzled dog could bite, it would, and the chained prisoner would run away. The truth is that I am a villain – a bad man, full of anger.

Conrad: Use your anger to make trouble then.

Don John: I will, be sure of it. Anger is all I have.

[Enter Borachio] What's your news, Borachio?

Borachio: I've just left the fine dinner that's going on. Leonato has put on great entertainment for your brother, Don Pedro. And I have news of a coming marriage.

Don John: Can I use this news to make trouble? Who is the fool who's going to ruin[35] his life?

Borachio: He is your brother's favourite soldier.

Don John: Do you mean that good-looking young man, Claudio?

Borachio: That's right.

Don John: A fine young man! Who's the lucky girl?

Borachio: It's Hero, Leonato's daughter and his only heir.

Don John: Well, Claudio certainly wants the best. How did you find out about this?

Borachio: I was preparing one of the rooms for the dance when the prince and Claudio walked past, talking very seriously. I hid behind a curtain and this is what I heard. Don Pedro, disguised by his mask, will pretend[36] to be Claudio and dance with Hero. He will court[37] her and win her love. Then he'll give her to Claudio.

Don John: Let's join the others. I can make plenty of trouble out of this. That fine soldier, Claudio, was the reason I became my brother's enemy. This is a good chance for me to get my revenge[38]. How I'll enjoy that! Are you both on my side[P]? Will you help me?

Conrad: We are yours till death, my lord.

Don John: Then let's go in to supper. The sight of my sad face will make everyone smile! What a pity the cook didn't poison[39] the food! Let's see what trouble we can cause.

Borachio: We are with you, my lord!

[Exit]

Act 2, Scene 1

[Enter Leonato, Antonio, Beatrice and Hero, with her gentlewomen[40], Margaret and Ursula]

Leonato: Was Don John at supper with us?

Antonio: I didn't see him.

Beatrice: What a sad look that gentleman has! He makes me feel ill to look at him.

Hero: He is certainly a very unhappy man.

Beatrice: One good man could be made by putting Don John and Benedick together. Don John stands there like a statue and says nothing. Benedick, on the other hand, never stops talking. He's like a little child.

Leonato: Yes. That's true. So we could put half of Benedick's tongue in Don John's mouth and half of John's sad look on Signor Benedick's face!

Beatrice: Add a good body and plenty of money and you have one fine man. That man could have any woman in the world – if she wanted him, of course.

Leonato: I must say, niece, you will never get a husband if you talk about men like that!

Antonio: I agree. Her tongue is far too sharp.

Beatrice: My sharp tongue will save me from giving any man sharp horns, thank God. But I'd rather have a husband with horns than a husband with a beard. I'd prefer to sleep on a rough[41] blanket.

Leonato: What about a husband without a beard?

Beatrice: He'd be no use to me at all. Unless I put him in a dress and made him my gentlewoman! So, beard or no beard? Neither, thank you very much. I'd rather die unmarried and childless and go to Hell than have a husband of any kind.

Leonato: Then down to Hell you will have to go.

Beatrice: Only to the gate. The devil will be sitting there, wearing his horns, like a wronged husband. 'Go up to Heaven,

21

Beatrice!' the devil will say. 'We don't take worthy virgins[42] here!' So up I'll go to St Peter who sits at the gates of Heaven. He'll welcome me in and show me where the unmarried people sit. I'll join them and we'll talk together happily for the rest of time!

Antonio: [To Hero] Well niece, I hope you will obey your father.

Beatrice: Yes, that's right, cousin Hero. Accept your father's choice of husband – if the young man is good-looking, of course.

Leonato: I hope you find a man who will suit you as a husband too, niece.

Beatrice: God made the first man from earth[43], uncle. That's not good enough for me.

Leonato: [To Hero] Daughter, remember what I told you. If Don Pedro speaks to you of marriage, listen to him.

Beatrice: Yes, cousin, dance to his tune. We women must always dance to the music men play for us. When we are in love, that music changes and the dance must change too. Before the wedding, the music is fast and exciting. The wedding itself needs a slower tune and a calmer dance. After the wedding, things change again until, faster and faster, we dance our lives away!

Leonato: You see things clearly, niece.

Beatrice: My eyes are good enough to see a church, uncle!

Leonato: Here come the dancers and musicians. It's time to put on our masks!

[Enter Don Pedro, Claudio, Benedick, Balthasar, Don John, Borachio, Margaret and Ursula, all wearing masks. The music plays and people begin to dance in pairs]

Don Pedro: [To Hero] Lady, will you dance with me?

Hero: If you dance well, sir, and don't talk too much.
And if you let me dance away at the end.

Don Pedro: As long as I go with you. Do you agree?

22

Lady, will you dance with me?

Hero: Only if your face is better looking than your mask. You may be too old for me.

Don Pedro: Not too old to talk of love. Listen …

[They dance away. Balthasar and Margaret come forward]

Balthasar: Well, I wish you liked me!

Margaret: Do you? I have many faults.

Balthasar: I don't care. I will love you anyway.

Margaret: Well, as long as you are a good dancer …

Balthasar: I am. I am.

Margaret: And as long as you do not bother me after the dance …

Balthasar: I'll make the most of it^p, then.

[They dance away]

Ursula: *[To her dance partner]* I know who you are. You are Signor Antonio.

Antonio: No, I am not.

Ursula: Yes, I think you are. Your head is shaking just like his.

Antonio: I'm pretending to be him. Don't I do it well?

Ursula: You *must* be Antonio – I recognize that wit and you dance well too!

[They dance away together. Beatrice and Benedick come forward as they dance]

Beatrice: Will you not tell me who told you that about me?

Benedick: No, I'm sorry, I can't.

Beatrice: Won't you even tell me who you are?

Benedick: No, not now.

Beatrice: They said that my words were scornful and not witty at all. That's what Signor Benedick says.

Benedick: Who's he?

Beatrice: I'm quite sure you know him.

Benedick: And I'm quite sure I don't.

Beatrice: Didn't he ever make you laugh?

Benedick: Never. Tell me who he is.

Beatrice: Well, he is Don Pedro's fool – and not a very funny one, either. The only thing he is good at is making up lies about people. Only the worst kind of men enjoy his jokes because they are stupid rather than witty. This Benedick first makes men laugh, then they want to beat him. I am sure that he's here somewhere. I wish he had tried to speak to me!

Beatrice: *Why, he is the prince's jester, a very dull fool, only his gift is in devising impossible slanders. None but libertines delight in him, and the commendation is not in his wit, but in his villainy, for he both pleaseth men and angers them, and then they laugh at him and beat him.*

jester = someone who makes jokes
devising = thinking of
slanders = speaks badly of
libertines = law-breakers
commendation = praise
villainy = bad jokes
pleaseth = pleases

Benedick: When I meet the gentleman, I'll tell him what you've said about him.
Beatrice: Please do. He'll try to say a few witty things about me, no one will laugh and then he'll get so angry that he won't be able to eat. Now don't stop dancing! We must keep up with the leaders.
Benedick: Let's follow where they lead then.
Beatrice: Only if they are going the right way!
[The musicians play another tune. Everyone dances away except Don John, Borachio and Claudio]
Don John: *[To Borachio]* I'm sure my brother is courting Hero for himself. He's talking to her father now. Hero has gone off with her gentlewomen and there's only one masked dancer left.
Borachio: And that's Claudio, I'm sure.
Don John: *[To Claudio]* Aren't you Signor Benedick?

Claudio: That's right, I am.

Don John: Signor, I know you are a favourite with my brother. He is deeply in love with Hero and I beg you to make him change his mind. The girl is not good enough for him. I am sure you will be doing the right thing by telling him so.

Claudio: How do you know Don Pedro loves her?

Don John: I heard him tell her so.

Borachio: And so did I. He said he'd like to marry her tonight!

Don John: [*To Borachio*] Let's go and have a drink.

[*Exit Don John and Borachio*]

Claudio: [*To himself*] I told those two that I was Benedick,
But their bad news was heard by Claudio's ears.
It's clear the prince wants Hero for himself.
Friendship is strong until love comes along.
A man in love should only trust himself,
For beauty has a magic all of its own that
Gives desire its power. I knew that to be true
But I could not believe that this would happen.
So, goodbye Hero! You are not for me!

Claudio: *Friendship is constant in all other things*
Save in the office and affairs of love.
Therefore all hearts in love use their own tongues,
Let every eye negotiate for itself
And trust no agent, for beauty is a witch
Against whose charms faith melteth into blood.

constant = faithful
save = except for
negotiate = make decisions
agent = helper
charms = magic power
faith = honesty
melteth = melts
blood = desires

[Enter Benedick]

Benedick: Count Claudio!

Claudio: Yes, I'm here.

Benedick: Will you come with me?

Claudio: Why? Where are you taking me?

Benedick: Where you can mourn[44] for your lost love. For you must wear mourning, Count. The prince has taken your Hero.

Claudio: He is welcome to her.

Benedick: That is the best way to look at it. But did you really think the prince would act like that?

Claudio: Leave me alone!

Benedick: *I* haven't done anything wrong! Don't blame *me*.

Claudio: If you won't go, I'll go myself.

[Exit Claudio]

Benedick: Poor man, he wants to be alone and I have things to think about too. Does my Lady Beatrice really think I am a fool? I thought she knew me better than that. I cannot believe that everyone thinks of me in the same way. No, it's just her opinion. I'll get my revenge – be sure of that!

[Enter Don Pedro]

Don Pedro: Have you seen Count Claudio, Signor?

Benedick: Yes, Prince, and I have been telling him the latest news – that you have courted Hero for yourself. I told Claudio that it was all his own fault. He was like a silly school boy who finds a bird's nest[45]. He shows it to his friend and the friend steals it, of course. Claudio should have kept his good news a secret. He should be beaten for letting you win this prize!

Don Pedro: No, no! I do not want Hero for myself. I was courting her for Claudio.

Benedick: So you *are* an honest man. Thank God.

Don Pedro: Lady Beatrice is angry with you. She danced with a gentleman who told her how you had insulted[46] her.

Benedick: Not as badly as she had insulted *me*! Of course, she thought that she was dancing with a stranger.

27

Don Pedro: What did Beatrice say about you? Do tell me.

Benedick: She said I was called the prince's fool, that all my jokes were bad ones and no one laughed at them – that's what she said. I had to stand there and listen to her. Every word she spoke was like a dagger[47]. Her words were killing me. I would not marry her even to live in Heaven. Beatrice makes trouble wherever she goes. If only someone would put a muzzle on her and shut her up! Until then, we'd all be better off in Hell!

[Enter Beatrice, Leonato and Hero]

Don Pedro: Look, she's coming now.

Benedick: *[To Don Pedro] Please,* my lord, send me on a journey as far away from here as possible – I cannot be in the same room as Lady Beatrice! Order me to do any difficult job for you – whether it takes me north, south, east or west! I'll go to the other side of the world, where people walk upside down! I'll go to Asia to cut down a tree. I'll bring you a hair from the beard of Kubla Khan, great king of the east. I'll go all the way to Africa! Anything rather than talk to that terrible woman with her awful tongue. Prince, you must have *something* that I can do!

Don Pedro: Yes – stay here with me. Let me enjoy your company.

Benedick: Oh, God, sir, no. You are serving tongue and that's a dish that makes me ill!

[Exit Benedick]

Don Pedro: Oh dear, I thought he had given you his heart!

Beatrice: If he ever did, then I have lost it. We did agree to be friends for a time and my heart was twice as loving as his. But he did not play fair, so I took my heart back again and gave him back his own.

Don Pedro: You have won the war of words, lady. Your words have really upset Signor Benedick. He'll have to give up and lie down now.

Beatrice: But I'm still standing! His words aren't enough to make me lie down next to him, I'm glad to say. You wanted to see Count Claudio – here he is.

[Enter Claudio]

Don Pedro: You look sad, Count. What's the matter?

Claudio: I am not sad.

Don Pedro: Sick, then?

Beatrice: With jealousy. And only you can end it.

Don Pedro: I think that you are right, lady, but Claudio has no cause to be jealous of me. Count, I courted Hero in your name and now she is yours. I have told her father and he agrees to the marriage. Now name your wedding day and may you be happy!

Leonato: Count Claudio, my daughter, Hero, who's my only heir, is yours. The prince has arranged it all and I agree to it.

Beatrice: Speak, Claudio. It's your turn to talk.

Claudio: I am too happy to say a word. *[To Hero]* You are mine and I am yours, all yours. I am very happy.

Beatrice: *[To Hero]* Say something, cousin! Or stop *him* talking, with a kiss!

Don Pedro: You certainly have a happy nature, Lady Beatrice.

Beatrice: That is true and it keeps me out of trouble! My cousin *is* talking now. I am sure she is telling Claudio how much she loves him.

Claudio: *[Laughing]* You are right, cousin. She is.

Beatrice: Thank God for marriage then! Soon everyone will have a husband, except me. I've got no chance. I sit in the sun too much. A beautiful lady must have a white skin – you all know that.

Don Pedro: I'll get you a husband, Lady Beatrice.

Beatrice: Just like your father 'got' himself good sons? Have you any brothers? They would make good husbands.

Don Pedro: What about me for a husband, lady?

Beatrice: No, my lord. Not unless I could have a cheaper husband as well. You are a prince, and too expensive to use

You are mine and I am yours, all yours.

every day. But oh, please don't take me seriously. I'm sorry. I make a joke of everything.

Don Pedro: I love your jokes. You were born at a merry time.

Beatrice: At that time, my mother cried, but I was born under a dancing star and that gave me a happy heart. Hero and Claudio – be happy too!

Leonato: Niece, you have some things to do for me …

Beatrice: I'll go at once. Please excuse me, Prince.

[Exit Beatrice]

Don Pedro: She certainly does have a happy heart.

Leonato: I have never seen her sad. If she has unhappy dreams, she wakes up laughing.

Don Pedro: She can't stand the thought of a husband.

Leonato: You are right. She mocks any man who tries to court her.

Don Pedro: She would make a perfect wife for Benedick.

Leonato: Oh, no! They would talk themselves mad after only a week of marriage.

Don Pedro: Count Claudio, when do you plan to marry?

Claudio: Tomorrow, my lord. Time will go so slowly until we are married.

Leonato: There are so many things to be done before the wedding. Wait until next Monday. That's exactly a week.

Don Pedro: You look unhappy, Claudio, but I have a plan to make the time go quickly. It is this: to make Beatrice and Benedick fall deeply in love with each other. I know that sounds impossible, but if everyone helps, we can do it.

Leonato: I'll help you, my lord.

Claudio: Me too.

Don Pedro: Will you help too, gentle Hero?

Hero: Help to find my cousin a good husband? Yes, I will.

Don Pedro: Benedick won't be a *bad* husband. He is from a good family; he is brave and honest. I'll show you how to make your cousin Beatrice fall in love with him. At the same time,

we men will trick[48] Benedick into loving *her*. We shall be doing the work of Cupid, the little god of love. Come with me and I'll tell you my plan.
[Exit]

Don Pedro: *I will teach you how to humour your cousin that she shall fall in love with Benedick, and I, with your two helps, will so practise on Benedick, that, in despite of his quick wit and his queasy stomach, he shall fall in love with Beatrice. If we can do this, Cupid is no longer an archer; his glory shall be ours, for we are the only love-gods.*

humour = influence, trick
practise = work
in despite of = in spite of, despite
queasy stomach = resistance, coldness
glory = victory

Act 2, Scene 2

[Enter Don John and Borachio]

Don John: So, Count Claudio is to marry Leonato's daughter.

Borachio: That's what *he* thinks, but I can stop him.

Don John: Then do it any way you can. I am sick to death of Claudio. Any problem you can put in his way makes my life happier. How will you stop this marriage?

Borachio: Not honestly, my lord. I will do it so secretly that no one will think it's my fault.

Don John: Tell me your plan.

Borachio: I have known Margaret, Hero's gentlewoman, for at least a year. She will do anything for me.

Don John: Go on.

Borachio: At any hour of the night, I can get Margaret to look out of Hero's bedroom window.

Don John: How will that put an end to Hero's marriage?

Borachio: I leave the details of the plan to you. Talk to your brother. Poison his mind in any way you like. Tell him you have made a mistake. Praise the honest Claudio and say that Hero is not a worthy wife for him. Say that she has courted other men – lots of them.

Don John: How do I get my brother to believe that? What proof[49] do I have?

Borachio: Enough to hurt your brother, to make Claudio unhappy, to ruin Hero and kill Leonato with shame.

Don John: I'll do anything to get that result.

Borachio: Then find a good time to speak to Don Pedro and Claudio together. Tell them that you know Hero loves *me*. Tell them how much you love and respect both of them. The marriage would bring your brother shame because he arranged it. Say that Hero is not a virgin and she doesn't care who she courts.

Don John: Will they really believe that?

Borachio: Claudio has a jealous heart. The night before the wedding, bring your brother and Claudio to stand outside Leonato's house. It will be dark, but they will see me leave from Hero's bedroom window. They will hear Margaret say goodbye to 'Claudio' with loving words. They will hear me call her 'Hero'. That should be enough to stop the wedding!

Don John: What about Hero herself?

Borachio: She will be away from home. I shall make sure of that. Claudio's jealous heart will tell him that Hero is false to him and all men. The wedding will be stopped.

Don John: If you are clever enough to make this plan work, I'll pay you one thousand ducats.

Borachio: Do what I say and it will work!

[Exit]

Act 2, Scene 3

[Leonato's garden. Enter Benedick. He sits down and starts talking to himself]

Benedick: How love changes a man! I'm talking about Claudio, of course. He used to laugh to see a man in love, but now he is in love himself! He was always interested in war and being a soldier. Now all he thinks about is fine new clothes. He used to speak simply, like an honest man – like a soldier, but now he talks without end about love, always about love. Could that happen to me? No, I don't think so, because no woman is worthy of my love. One woman may be fair, another clever and the third very good, but I'm not interested in any one of them. The woman *I* loved would have to be all three – fair, clever *and* good too. But that's not all. She'd have to be rich, I'm sure of that. Quiet too – but able to speak well. And, of course, she would always have to agree with me. What else? Yes, I'd like her to be a good musician. Most important of all, she must be beautiful, or I would never be able to look at her! What about her hair? It can be any colour – as long as it's natural!

[Enter Don Pedro, Leonato, Claudio and Balthasar]

Here come the prince and Signor Love. I'll hide myself.

[Benedick hides behind some trees]

Don Pedro: Let's sit down here and listen to the song again.

Claudio: Yes, my good lord. The evening is so quiet,
Because it is waiting to hear sweet music.

Don Pedro: *[Very quietly, to Claudio]* Now, can you see where Benedick is hiding?

Claudio: Of course, my lord. And when the music's over
We'll catch that clever fool with clever words.

Don Pedro: Come on, Balthasar. Sing your song again.

Balthasar: Oh, my good lord, please do not order me
To shame sweet music for a second time.

Don Pedro: The best is always slow to praise itself,

So I must court you and your voice as lovers do.

Balthasar: Because you talk of courting, I will sing.
Lovers often praise the one they love,
Just as you praise me and my poor voice.

Don Pedro: Now that's enough, your song must speak for you.

Balthasar: Then please note[50] this – my notes are not worth noting.

Don Pedro: So, no more words.
We'll note your notes and nothing else will do!

Balthasar: *[Singing]* Cry no more ladies, cry no more.
All men tell lies, they always do.
They change what they have said before
The words they speak are never true.
Then no more tears, send men away
You're happier on your own.
Sing happy songs all through the day
You're better off alone!

Don Pedro: That's a good song!

Balthasar: But a bad singer, my lord.

Don Pedro: No, no, you sing well enough.

Benedick: *[To himself]* I don't agree. If a dog had made a noise like that, someone would have killed it! I hope that a bad voice will not bring bad luck.

Don Pedro: Find some more good songs. I'd like you to sing again tomorrow night, outside Lady Hero's window.

Balthasar: I'll do my best[P], my lord.

[Exit Balthasar]

Don Pedro: *[In a loud voice]* Tell me, Leonato, didn't you say earlier that Lady Beatrice is in love with Signor Benedick?

Claudio: Is that true? I did not think that lady would ever fall in love.

Leonato: I agree and I thought she hated Benedick.

Benedick: *[To himself]* Is that the way the wind is blowing?

Leonato: I can't understand it either, but she is a woman deeply in love.

*Tell me, Leonato, didn't you say earlier
Lady Beatrice is in love with Signor Benedick?*

Don Pedro: Are you sure that she's not pretending to be in love?

Claudio: You may be right.

Leonato: Pretending? No, it's not possible. No woman could act as well as that. Beatrice has told my daughter, Hero, how she feels.

Claudio: That's true, she has.

Don Pedro: That's amazing. I didn't think any man would win her heart.

Leonato: I thought the same. And especially not Benedick.

Benedick: This must be true if old Leonato believes it.

Don Pedro: But has Beatrice told Benedick how she feels?

Leonato: No – and she says she never will. But she did begin to write him a letter. She stayed up night after night, filling sheet after sheet of paper with her writing.

Claudio: Hero made a good joke about that. Tell the prince what she said.

Leonato: That 'Beatrice' and 'Benedick' were together on the same 'sheet' at last.

Don Pedro: *[Laughing]* What did Beatrice do then?

Leonato: She was angry and tore the letter up!

Don Pedro: Oh dear! Poor lady!

Leonato: She tore the letter into a thousand pieces. She was very angry with herself for writing so honestly about her feelings. She knew that Benedick would laugh if he ever read the letter. So she could never, never send it.

Leonato: *O, she tore the letter into a thousand halfpence, railed at herself, that she should be so immodest to write to one that she knew would flout her. 'I measure him,' says she, 'by my own spirit, for I should flout him if he writ to me, yea, though I love him, I should.'*

halfpence = very small pieces
railed at = shouted at

flout = reject
measure = judged by
spirit = character

Claudio: Then Beatrice fell down on her knees, praying and crying: 'Oh, my dear Benedick! How I love and hate him!'

Leonato: It's all true. My daughter saw her and she's worried that Beatrice will go mad.

Don Pedro: If Beatrice won't tell Benedick, then we should.

Claudio: Why? He would laugh at Beatrice and make her even more unhappy.

Don Pedro: I think you are right. She is a sweet lady and a good woman.

Claudio: And she is very sensible.

Don Pedro: Except in her love for Benedick!

Leonato: No one is sensible when they are in love. But I am her uncle. I should try to help her.

Don Pedro: If Beatrice had fallen in love with me, I would have married her myself! Do tell Benedick what has happened. See what he has to say.

Leonato: Are you sure?

Claudio: Hero thinks that Beatrice will die, whatever happens. She will die if Benedick doesn't love her, but she will die rather than tell him about her love. And, last of all, if he courts her, she will die rather than speak kindly to him.

Don Pedro: I think Hero's right. If Beatrice shows any kindness to Benedick, he will scorn her.

Claudio: Benedick is good-looking and he's clever too.

Don Pedro: Yes, and sometimes he says things which almost seem witty.

Leonato: And I understand that he is a brave soldier.

Don Pedro: That is very true. But he keeps out of trouble and prefers to make a joke rather than argue with anyone – except Beatrice, of course. I'm sorry for your niece. Shall we find Benedick and tell him of Beatrice's love for him?

Leonato: That's not a good idea. Her feelings may change again.

Don Pedro: Very well. We'll wait. Let's see what your daughter tells us. I like Benedick very much, but I think Beatrice is too good for him. I wish he could see that.

Leonato: Dinner will be ready, my lord. Let's go inside.

Claudio: [Quietly] Trust me. Benedick is sure to fall in love with her now.

Don Pedro: [Quietly] Hero and her gentlewoman must play the same trick on Beatrice. They will know what to do. What a joke it will be! Both Beatrice and Benedick will think that the other is in love. Then they will find out that isn't true. For the first time in their lives, they will have nothing to say! First, we'll send Beatrice to call Benedick in to dinner.

[Exit Don Pedro, Leonato and Claudio]

Benedick: [Coming to the front of the stage] All that I have heard here must be true. Hero would not lie and she knows Beatrice well. They all feel sorry for her. I shall be blamed[51] if I do not take her feelings seriously. Does she really love me? If so, then I should love her in return, but no one thinks I will. No, they say I am too proud. They all think I will scorn her love. But, on the other hand, she will never tell me the truth. So it is all up to me[p]. I must forget my pride. Happy is the man who learns his faults and tries to change them. They say the lady's fair, and I can see that for myself. She's good, too. We all agree on that. Sensible? Well, yes, apart from loving me. Was that a wise decision of hers or a foolish one? Well, I don't care either way. I have made up my mind[p] to love her and to marry her! I had never wanted to marry, but who cares? Forget what I said about love in the past. A man may change his mind as he gets older. When I said I would die a bachelor, I did not think that I would live long enough to be a married man! Here comes Beatrice now. How beautiful love makes her look!

[Enter Beatrice]

Beatrice: I did not want to come, but I have been told to bring you in to dinner.

Benedick: Thank you for taking the trouble, fair Beatrice.

Beatrice: It's no trouble.

Benedick: You must be pleased to do it then.

Beatrice: Pleased? You must please yourself. If you are not hungry, don't come to dinner. Goodbye.

[Exit Beatrice]

Benedick: 'No trouble' and 'You must please yourself'. Yes, lady, I will. She is in love and so am I! I will go and get a little picture of her and carry it with me always!

[Exit]

Act 3, Scene 1

[Enter Hero and her two gentlewomen, Margaret and Ursula]
Hero: Good Margaret, go quickly to the sitting room.
Beatrice is there, talking to the prince and Claudio.
Tell her that Ursula and myself are in the garden
Discussing the love that someone has for her.
Beatrice must hide – she must hear but not be seen.
There is a place behind the trees – you know it well –
Where my dear friend can hear this talk of love.
Your job is easy – leave Beatrice there alone
And we will do the rest.
Margaret: I understand. I'll send her there at once.
[Exit Margaret]
Hero: Now Ursula, when Beatrice is nearby,
We'll walk together up and down this path
And all our talk will be of Benedick
And of his love for Beatrice. So, in that way,
We'll do the work of Cupid, god of love.
[Enter Beatrice, who hides herself]
Now Beatrice is listening – are you ready?
Ursula: *[Quietly]* We're like two fishermen who watch the fish
They want to catch swim through the water.
My lady Beatrice must be caught with words,
Just as the golden fish is caught with flies.
Hero: *[Speaking very loudly]* I know she'll scorn him, Ursula,
and his love.
Ursula: But are you sure that Benedick loves Beatrice?
Hero: The prince believes it and my Claudio too.
Ursula: Do they want you to tell her, lady?
Hero: That's what they said, but I did not agree.
Beatrice must never know about his love.
Ursula: But Benedick should have a happy marriage
And so should Beatrice too. Don't you agree?

Hero: I do, but Beatrice is too proud to change her mind.
She scorns all thoughts of love for Benedick.
The only love she has is for herself.
Ursula: If she finds out that Benedick's in love
She'll make a joke of it, I'm sure of that.
Hero: However good or brave a man may be,
Beatrice will be sure to make a fool of him.
If he is fair, she'll say he's like a woman.
And if his skin is dark, more like a devil.
If tall, his head's too small, if short, too big.
And if he talks too much that is a fault.
But then a quiet man has no ideas at all.
So Beatrice has no praise for any man.
She scorns them all and that will never change!
Ursula: Yes, you're right. She's truly full of scorn.
Hero: But who will tell her so? I will not do it.
Beatrice would laugh at me and mock me.
Benedick must die from the quick fire of love
Not slowly from the words of Beatrice.
Ursula: Tell her the truth. Find out what she thinks.
Hero: I have a better plan. I'll talk to Benedick.
I'll tell him he must fight against his love.
To help him, I'll say bad things about Beatrice
To make him change his mind about the lady.
Ursula: But that's not fair on her! She is too clever.
She knows that Benedick's a worthy man.
She surely won't refuse him!
Hero: Benedick is the finest man in Italy –
Except for my dear Claudio, of course!
Ursula: Forgive me for saying what I think, my lady –
I think Signor Benedick's the better man.
He is witty, brave – good-looking too.
I think he's the finest man in Italy!
Hero: He is well liked, I can agree with that.

Ursula: I'll say no more. When is your wedding, lady?
Hero: Some day very soon. Let's go inside.
Help me to choose the headdress[52] I shall wear.
[The two women move away]
Ursula: Beatrice has been caught, I'm sure, just like a fish.
Hero: If you are right, then loving goes by chance.
We are all part of Cupid's clever dance.
[Exit Hero and Ursula. Beatrice comes forward]
Beatrice: My ears are burning[P]! Can their words be true?
Am I so proud? Am I so full of scorn?
Then goodbye scorn, goodbye proud words!
They are no use to me, for I must love
Where I am loved. We shall be married.
What I have just heard I will believe.
His love is strong and it must be returned.
[Exit]

Act 3, Scene 2

[Enter Don Pedro, Claudio, Benedick and Leonato]

Don Pedro: I'll stay until after your wedding, Claudio, then I must go back to Aragon.

Claudio: I'll go back with you, sir, if you would like me to.

Don Pedro: That would be a fine start to your marriage! No, I'll take Benedick with me. He'll be good company, because he's full of fun. Benedick has fooled Cupid several times and his heart is as strong as it ever was. He talks a lot, I know, but what Benedick's tongue says, is what he really thinks.

Benedick: Friends, I am not the man I was.

Leonato: You are looking rather sad.

Claudio: I hope he's in love!

Leonato: No, no. Benedick couldn't be in love. If he's sad, it must be because he's short of money[P].

Benedick: I have toothache.

Leonato: Get the tooth taken out, then. No problem.

Benedick: It's easy for you to say that!

Claudio: I still say he's in love.

Leonato: I can't see any of the usual signs.

Claudio: I don't agree. He's always changing his clothes, and he brushes his hat every morning. His beard has gone too.

Leonato: You're right and he looks younger without it.

Don Pedro: And, what's more, he's wearing perfume[53]! That's the smell of love itself!

Claudio: Yes, perfume's a sure sign of love!

Leonato: But the surest sign of all is that he's sad.

Claudio: Don't forget the perfume! He never used to wear it.

Don Pedro: And perhaps a little make-up? He's wearing some of that too. That makes it certain he's in love.

Claudio: Sad, slow music is all he wants to hear – as all true lovers do.

Don Pedro: That settles it[P]! He's in love, for sure.

45

I still say he's in love.

Claudio: And I know who loves *him*.

Don Pedro: That's what I really want to be sure of. I don't think she knows what he's like.

Claudio: No, I agree, but she's dying with love for him.

Don Pedro: She'll die on her back, then!

Benedick: None of this is helping my toothache! Good Leonato, I'd like to speak to you alone. I don't want these jokers hearing what I have to say.

[Exit Benedick and Leonato]

Don Pedro: He's going to tell Leonato about Beatrice!

Claudio: I am sure you're right. By now, Beatrice has heard Hero and Ursula talking about Benedick's love for her. So when those two bears – Beatrice and Benedick – meet each other, they will not bite!

[Enter Don John]

Don John: God save you, my lord and brother.

Don Pedro: Good evening to you, brother.

Don John: If you have a moment, I should like to speak to you.

Don Pedro: Do you mean in private?

Don John: If you don't mind. But Count Claudio can hear what I have to say. It is his problem, as well as yours.

Don Pedro: What do you mean?

Don John: Count Claudio, is tomorrow your wedding day?

Don Pedro: You know very well it is.

Claudio: If there is a problem, tell me about it.

Don John: You may think I don't like you, but don't decide just yet. Hear my news first, Claudio. My brother, your good friend, has helped you with this marriage. I'm sorry to say that was a bad mistake. He has taken a lot of trouble, but it's all been for nothing.

Don John: *You may think I love you not: let that appear hereafter, and aim better at me by that I will now manifest. For*

47

my brother, I think he holds you well, and in dearness of heart, hath holp to effect your ensuing marriage; surely, suit ill spent, and labour ill bestowed.

aim = think
manifest = show
holp = helped
effect = arrange
ensuing = coming
suit = effort
ill = badly

Don Pedro: For nothing? I don't understand.

Don John: That's why I'm here. I have to tell you – the lady has been unfaithful.

Claudio: Unfaithful? My Hero?

Don John: *Your* Hero? No! She's every man's Hero.

Claudio: Unfaithful? To *me*?

Don John: To every man. The word is too good for her. Say nothing more until I give you proof. Stand with me tonight, under her bedroom window. As we hide there, you will see a man climb up into her room – and stay there for some time. And remember, it's the night before your wedding! Can you still love her after that? If you can, then marry her tomorrow. But the right thing to do, would be to change your mind.

Claudio: Can this really be true?

Don Pedro: I really can't believe it.

Don John: If you can't believe what you see, then keep quiet. But if you do what I say, I shall give you more than enough proof. Then you must make your own decision.

Claudio: If I see proof that Hero is unfaithful, I will not marry her in the church tomorrow. No, I shall shame her there before her friends.

Don Pedro: I helped you to court her. I shall help you to shame her too.

Don John: I'll say nothing more. You must see for yourselves. Stay calm until tonight, then make your minds up.
Don Pedro: What an ending to the day!
Claudio: How everything good has changed!
Don John: But something terrible has been stopped! You'll say that too after tonight!
[Exit]

Act 3, Scene 3

[Enter Dogberry, Leader of the Watch[54]*, who is carrying a lantern*[55]*, Verges and the rest of the Watch, who are all old men]*

Dogberry: Are all these men honest?

Verges: They must be, sir. They have been chosen to look after this city.

Dogberry: That's right. If they weren't honest, they would all come to a terrible end.

Verges: Speak to them, neighbour. Ask them their names. Check that they know their job.

Dogberry: First, I must choose the leader. His job is to hold the lantern. He must challenge any villains too. Neighbour Seacole, you must be that man.

Seacole: Sir, I cannot read or write.

Dogberry: Never mind, just hold the lantern. If you see a man out walking, late at night, ask for his name. You don't have to write it down. Tell him to stop in the *prince's* name.

Seacole: And if he doesn't stop?

Dogberry: Then let him go. He is no friend of ours.

Verges: He's no friend to the prince, either. So don't worry about him, Neighbour Seacole.

Dogberry: Quite right. And you must be quiet, too. No talking or shouting!

1st Watchman: We could always sleep. Then we would be quiet.

Dogberry: That's a good idea. Now here's another thing. If you meet any men who are drunk, tell them to go home.

2nd Watchman: And if they won't go?

Dogberry: Then leave them alone and walk away. Do the same with any villain. Don't have anything to do with bad men. Keep the city quiet and be quiet yourselves. In that way, you will help our prince. Come, Verges. We'll leave the Watch to do their job.

1ˢᵗ Watchman: Right, sir. We'll sit here until two o'clock and then we'll go home to bed.

Dogberry: One more thing. Be sure that you watch Signor Leonato's house. There's a wedding there tomorrow. Lots of people will be coming and going. Keep your eyes open! Now goodnight, neighbours.

[Exit Dogberry and Verges. Enter Borachio and Conrad]

Borachio: Hey! Conrad!

1ˢᵗ Watchman: *[Quietly]* Let's listen.

Conrad: Here I am. What have you been doing, you villain?

Borachio: Come and stand over here, out of the rain. Then I'll tell you everything. It's a good story.

2ⁿᵈ Watchman: *[Quietly]* A villain? There's something wrong here, neighbours!

Borachio: Don John is a villain too, but he has paid me well. He has given me one thousand ducats for one night's work!

Conrad: One thousand ducats? Have you been drinking? Let's hear the truth.

Borachio: I *have* been drinking and why not? That is the truth. I've got lots of money now! I can buy what I like! I can dress in the latest fashion!

Conrad: Never mind about fashion. Tell me your story. What did you do for Don John?

Borachio: Here's the truth, then. Tonight, I courted Margaret, Lady Hero's gentlewoman, in the name of Hero. Margaret was looking out of Lady Hero's bedroom window. She said goodnight to me time after time and ... wait a minute, I am not telling this story in the right way. I should have told you that the prince, Claudio and that villain, my master, were all listening nearby.

Conrad: And they thought that Margaret was Hero?

Borachio: The prince and Claudio did, but that devil, my master, knew the truth. It was all his idea – to make Hero look unfaithful, make Claudio look a fool and to stop the wedding!

Conrad: Claudio believed all this?

Borachio: All of it! He was very, very angry. He plans to go to the church tomorrow and shame Hero there, before all her friends. He'll send her home without a husband. That's just what that devil, my master, wanted. He's a villain. Come on, let's go. It's raining harder now.

Borachio: *Two of them did, the prince and Claudio; but the devil, my master, knew she was Margaret; and partly by his oaths, which first possessed them, partly by the dark night, which did deceive them, but chiefly by the villainy, which did confirm any slander that Don John had made, away went Claudio enraged; swore he would meet her, as he was appointed, next morning at the temple, and there, before the whole congregation, shame her with what he saw over-night , and send her home again without a husband.*

oaths = statements
slander = negative comments
enraged = furious
congregation = group

1st Watchman: Devil? Villain? This is not right!

2nd Watchman: Stop there in the prince's name! We must take you with us.

[The watchmen hold Conrad and Borachio]

Borachio: Let me go!

Conrad: You have got this all wrong!

2nd Watchman: Don't say a word. You must come with us.

Conrad: Very well, then. You'll soon find that you have made a mistake. Then you'll all be in trouble!

[Exit the Watch, with Conrad and Borachio]

Stop there in the prince's name! We must take you with us.

Act 3, Scene 4

[Enter Hero, Margaret and Ursula]

Hero: Good Ursula, please wake up my cousin, Beatrice.

Ursula: I will, my lady.

Hero: Tell her to get up and come here. I need her.

Ursula: I'm on my way, lady.

[Exit Ursula]

Margaret: *[Looking at a headdress]* I think that your other headdress is better than this one.

Hero: I don't think so, Margaret. I'll wear this one.

Margaret: The other one *is* better. Your cousin is sure to agree with me.

Hero: Then she's a fool and so are you! I'm not going to change my mind!

Margaret: But I do like your wedding dress. It is really lovely. It's the latest fashion too.

Hero: Yes, I *am* pleased with the dress.

Margaret: You should be! Just look at it! The material's made of gold, with a design of pearls[56] and silver on the skirt. The under-skirt is a thin, silver material and so are the tight sleeves[57]. These double sleeves are so fashionable now and they are covered with pearls too. The skirt's a very clever shape. Yes, this dress is just perfect!

Hero: I hope I shall be happy wearing it. My heart feels very heavy.

Margaret: Never mind. It will soon feel heavier by the weight of a man – your husband I mean!

Hero: Shame on you[P]! What a thing to say!

Margaret: There is no shame in saying that, lady, if the right husband finds the right wife. Then you will be light-hearted!

[Enter Beatrice]

Hero: Good morning, cousin.

Beatrice: *[Sadly]* Good morning, sweet Hero.

Hero: What's the matter? You sound ill.

Beatrice: I am.

Margaret: Let's all sing 'Light of love' – that's a light, cheerful tune. And I'll dance to it. After all, we don't want anything too heavy, do we, Hero?

Beatrice: If love makes your heart as light as your feet, you'll say yes to any man. That will get you into trouble, one day!

Margaret: No, lady. I'll use my light feet to run away!

Beatrice: *[To Hero]* It's nearly five o'clock, cousin. You should be dressed by now. Oh dear, I do feel ill.

Margaret: Because you do not feel the weight of a husband! Is that your problem?

Beatrice: What are you going on about, you silly girl?

Margaret: That we can all go on to our own true love!

Hero: Claudio sent me these perfumed gloves. Do smell them, cousin.

Beatrice: I can't smell anything. My cold is too bad.

Margaret: And it's too bad that you are too cold, lady. Too cold to love, I mean.

Beatrice: And since when has your tongue been so clever?

Margaret: Since yours became so sad and silly, lady. You have become too sad-hearted. Someone has to make people laugh.

Beatrice: I don't feel like laughing. I am too ill.

Margaret: Then you need medicine. Holy-thistle is a plant that is good for the sad-hearted. *Carduus benedictus*, the doctors call it.

Beatrice: Benedic – tus? That name again! What makes you think of benedictus? Are you trying to tell me something?

Margaret: No, no! Of course not. I'm not trying to say that you are in love, if that's what you think. All I know is that Benedick thought he would never love, and said he would never marry. But now he's changed his mind. And the same thing might happen to you. I don't know how, but it will!

Beatrice: Please stop all this silly talk for a minute!

It's nearly five o'clock, cousin. You should be dressed by now.

Margaret: It's not silly, it's the truth!

[Enter Ursula]

Ursula: Lady, you must get ready at once. The prince, the count, Signor Benedick, Don John and all the rest, have come to take you to the church.

Hero: Then all of you, come and help me dress!

[Exit Hero, Beatrice, Margaret and Ursula]

Act 3, Scene 5

[Enter Leonato, Dogberry and Verges]

Leonato: Good neighbours, what do you want to say to me?

Dogberry: I need to talk to you about something very private.

Leonato: Please say it quickly then. I am very busy today.

Dogberry: Yes, we know that you are busy. It is your daughter's wedding, sir. We'll tell you as quickly as we can, won't we, Neighbour Verges?

Verges: That's right. You must have a lot to do. You speak the truth, sir, and so do we. We are all honest men here. Some of us are old perhaps, but we all keep busy.

Dogberry: Yes, yes, I am a very honest man, and I am old too.

Leonato: Neighbours, I am keeping as calm as I can. But you really must tell me what you have to say to me. Please be quick.

Verges: Well, sir, then I will now tell you that our Watch has caught two villains. Yes, two of the worst villains in Messina. Very bad men, sir. I did not think that there were such bad men in this city! *Your* city, sir.

Leonato: I must ask you …

Dogberry: Neighbour Verges is a very old man, sir. Old men will go on talking, won't they? We both know that is the truth.

Leonato: I really must go.

Dogberry: But sir, you must see these men. You must question them this morning. That is the law, sir, as you know.

Leonato: Question them yourself. Then tell me what you found out later. Have a drink before you go. Thank you. Goodbye.

[Enter a messenger]

Messenger: My lord, they are all waiting for you at the church.

Leonato: I am ready. We'll go together.
[Exit Leonato and Messenger]
Dogberry: Go, good Verges and find Neighbour Oatcake. He is the best man in the Watch at reading and writing. I shall examine those villains myself and Neighbour Oatcake can write down everything they say. Meet me at the jail.
[Exit]

Act 4, Scene 1

[In the church. Enter Don Pedro, Don John, Leonato, Friar Francis, Claudio, Benedick, Hero and Beatrice and guests]

Leonato: Friar Francis, you are here to marry my daughter to Count Claudio. Please begin.

Friar Francis: Lady, you are here to marry the count.

Hero: I am.

Friar Francis: If either you or the count know of anything that should stop this marriage, tell me now.

Claudio: Do you know of anything, Hero?

Hero: No, my lord.

Friar Francis: And what about you, Count?

Leonato: I can answer that. Of course he doesn't.

Claudio: Wait just a minute. Let me ask you a question.
Are you, her father, here to give to me,
This sweet and worthy girl, Hero, your daughter?

Leonato: I give her to you gladly, my dear son.

Claudio: And what of the same worth can I give back to you?

Leonato: I know of nothing equal to my daughter.

Claudio: Take back your rubbish then, for she's worth nothing!
Hero may look honest, but she's not.
Her gentle smiles have fooled you and me too.
See how she stands there, looking at the ground!
Her face is like a mask, disguising shame itself.
She looks as though she's good, but she is not.
Your daughter's not a virgin – she's a spoilt fruit.

Leonato: What do you mean, my lord?

Claudio: Not to be married, that is what I mean.
Not to want to join myself to one I know is false.

Leonato: My dear good lord, perhaps you now regret[58]
Something that *you* have done.

Claudio: You mean to say that I have spoilt her
And that the fault is mine. That is not true.

60

I have loved Hero with a brother's love,
Respected her as I respect my sister.

Hero: Have I not seemed worthy of respect?

Claudio: 'Seemed' do you say? Then shame on you!
You *seemed* as good as any girl could be,
But now I know the truth – no man is safe
When you decide to take him to your bed.

Hero: You must be ill, my lord, to say such things!

Leonato: *[To Don Pedro]* Sweet prince, why are *you* silent?

Don Pedro: I am too angry to say anything.
I helped my good friend Claudio court this liar.
And that's brought shame on me.

Leonato: Do I hear these awful words, or am I dreaming?

Don John: Oh, you can hear them and they all are true.

Benedick: *[Quietly]* This does not sound much like a marriage!

Hero: True? Oh God!

Claudio: Leonato, am I really here?
Is this the prince? Is this the prince's brother?
Is this face Hero's? Do I see these things?

Leonato: Why do you ask these questions, my good lord?

Claudio: I want to ask your daughter just one more.
Tell her to speak the truth before her father.

Leonato: You hear him, Hero. You must tell the truth.

Hero: Why must I answer? I don't understand.

Claudio: I need to hear you answer to your name.

Hero: My name is Hero. There's no shame in that.

Claudio: Hero herself can bring shame to Hero.
Who was the man who spoke to you last night
At your own bedroom window after midnight?
If you are still a virgin, answer me.

Hero: I spoke to no man at that time, my lord.

Don Pedro: Then you are not a virgin, Hero.
I'm sorry, Leonato, you must hear me.
Myself, my brother, Claudio himself

All saw her, heard her, at that time last night
Talk to a villain at her bedroom window.
And that same man has told us he has been
With Hero in her room and in her bed,
More than a thousand times in secret.
Don John: Please do not speak of them, my brother.
The language you must use will be too shameful.
As shameful as your life, my pretty lady.
Claudio: The beauty of your face is just a mask
To cover all your ugly thoughts and plans.
So goodbye Hero, who makes beauty ugly
And hides her shame behind the sweetest smiles.
Because of you, I'll never love again.
When I see beauty, I shall turn away
Knowing there's no good in it at all.
Leonato: You all have daggers – use them now to kill me!
[Hero faints[59] and falls to the ground]
Beatrice: My dear cousin, what's the matter?
Don John: Let's go. The truth has been too much for her.
[Exit Don Pedro, Don John and Claudio]
Benedick: How is she?
Beatrice: I think she's dead. Hero, wake up! Help me, uncle!
Wake up, Hero! Uncle! Signor Benedick! Friar, help me!
Leonato: Don't try to wake her! Death is the best end for her
now.
Beatrice: Come on, cousin. Wake up!
Friar Francis: It's all right, lady.
[Hero opens her eyes]
Leonato: Can you still look at us, Hero?
Friar Francis: What do you mean? Why shouldn't she?
Leonato: Why? Isn't there a good reason why
When every living thing cries shame upon her?
Can she deny she's guilty when her face
Shows the whole world what she wants most to hide?

I think she's dead. Hero, wake up!

Do not live, Hero, look at me no more.
I am your father, but I hope you'll die.
If you can live with shame like this, I cannot
And my own shame will mean I'll have to kill you.
I used to wish that I'd had more than one
But now I wish I'd had no child at all.
Why was I ever glad that you were mine?
For now it seems, your shame is my shame too.
You were my only child to love and praise,
I only thought of you and not myself.
But now your beauty is as black as ink[60].
Not all the water in the salty sea
Can make it fresh and clean again.
Benedick: Good sir, calm down. I am so surprised
I don't know what to say.
Beatrice: And I am sure that all of this is lies!
Benedick: Then did you sleep in Hero's room last night?
Beatrice: No, I did not, although I usually do.
Leonato: That proves it then, there's no way out.
Would the two princes lie? Would Claudio?
His love made him cry as he thought of her shame.
So let Hero go! Let Hero die!
Friar Francis: First let me speak.
I have been silent for a special reason.
I've used my eyes to help me find the truth
About this lady. I have watched her face.
I've seen no guilty look, no sign at all
That she's done any wrong.
You know that I'm a man of great experience
Who can tell good from bad. So I tell you
The lady's without guilt or any shame.
This has all been a terrible mistake, I'm sure of it.
Leonato: Friar, you know that can't be true.
There's only one good thing to say about my daughter;

She's told no lies about her shameful life.
Why make excuses for her? Why cover up the truth?
Friar Francis: Lady, if you have had a lover, what's his name?
Hero: I've never had a lover. That's the truth.
Oh, my dear father, if you or anyone can prove
That I did any wrong last night, turn me away,
Hate me – kill me, any way you like!

> **Hero:** O, *my father,*
> *Prove you that any man with me conversed*
> *At hours unmet, or that I yesternight*
> *Maintained the change of words with any creature,*
> *Refuse me, hate me, torture me to death!*
>
> *unmet* = unsuitable
> maintained = had
> torture = hurt

Friar Francis: You *have* all made a terrible mistake. I'm sure
of it.
Benedick: Don Pedro is an honest man and so is Claudio.
Don John, the prince's brother, is a villain though.
If he can make any trouble, then he will.
Leonato: That may be so, but if they've told the truth,
I'll tear my girl to pieces with my hands.
If they've wronged her, I'll take revenge on them.
I may be old, but I have powerful friends.
The princes will not live to make more trouble.
Friar Francis: I have a better plan you should agree to.
Tell all the world your daughter Hero's dead.
Mourn her, put flowers on her tomb[61].
But keep her safely hidden, out of sight.
Leonato: Why should I do all this? What is the point?
Friar Francis: Well, first of all, people will feel unhappy.
But I want something more and it is this –

As time goes by, Hero will be remembered
Because her life was ended by hard words.
Count Claudio will know he's lost a prize
And he will mourn the worthy girl who's gone.
Then, day by day, his sadness will grow deeper
And he will blame himself for what has happened.
He will feel shame, because he has shamed Hero.
He will love her more in death than in her life.
Benedick: Signor Leonato, this is good advice.
Don Pedro and Count Claudio are my friends,
But I shall keep this plan a secret from them.
Leonato: I'll listen to you then. I'm too sad to argue.
Friar Francis: I'm glad to hear it. Let us leave at once.
All strange diseases need a clever doctor.
Come, lady, seem to die and dying you may live
To see your wedding day. Believe me and be strong.
[Exit Friar Francis, Hero and Leonato]
Benedick: Lady Beatrice, have you been crying all this time?
Beatrice: Yes and I'll go on crying for some time yet.
Benedick: I do not like to see you crying.
Beatrice: I don't care. I'm crying because I want to.
Benedick: I think your cousin has been wrongly blamed.
Beatrice: If anyone could help her, they would be my friend!
Benedick: What would this friend need to do?
Beatrice: That's easily answered, but who would do it?
Benedick: Is it something that a man could do?
Beatrice: Oh, yes, but that man isn't you.
Benedick: I love you more than anything else in the world.
Isn't that strange?
Beatrice: Yes, very strange. I could say that I love nothing as
much as you. Oh, don't believe that, but yet it's true – or is it?
What am I saying? My cousin, my poor cousin.
Benedick: I swear[62] on my sword, Beatrice, that you *do* love me.

Beatrice: Be careful. You may want to take those words back. What you swear to, must be true.

Benedick: Oh, it is. I'm not going to eat my words. And if any man calls me a liar, he'll have to eat my sword!

Beatrice: Are you quite sure that you won't eat your words?

Benedick: No – however well cooked they are. Listen: *I love you.*

Beatrice: Then God forgive me.

Benedick: For what, sweet Beatrice?

Beatrice: You have caught me at the right time. I was going to say 'I love you'.

Benedick: Then say it, please. Say it with all your heart.

Beatrice: I love you with so much of my heart that there is nothing left to say.

Benedick: I will do anything for you – anything at all!

Beatrice: Kill Claudio!

Benedick: No! Not for the world!

Beatrice: You kill *me* by saying that. Goodbye.

Benedick: Wait a minute, sweet Beatrice.

Beatrice: Not for one second! I'm going. You don't know the meaning of love. Let go of me!

Benedick: Beatrice …

Beatrice: I swear I will go.

Benedick: Then let's part as friends …

Beatrice: You think it's easier to be friends with me than fight my enemy!

Benedick: Is Claudio your enemy?

Beatrice: Has he not shown himself to be a villain? He has lied about, scorned and shamed my dear cousin. How I wish I were a man! He waited until the last minute, just as they were going to be married. And then, in front of everyone, he said such awful words about her – Oh God, if only I were a man! I would eat his heart in the market-place!

Benedick: Now, listen, Beatrice …

Beatrice: Talking with a man out of her window! A fine story!

Benedick: But, Beatrice, listen to me …

Beatrice: My dear, sweet Hero! She is wronged, she is scorned. She is ruined forever.

Benedick: Bea …

Beatrice: So that's how princes and counts behave! A count! A *sweet* man! A man made of sugar! If only I were a man or had a *real* man to help me! But where would I find one of those? Men are all talk – sweet talk and lies. Wishing won't make me a man, so I shall die crying as a woman must.

Benedick: Wait, sweet Beatrice. I swear by this hand that I love you.

Beatrice: If you love me, use your hand in another way.

Benedick: Are you sure in your heart that Count Claudio has wronged Hero?

Beatrice: As sure as I have a heart.

Benedick: That's all I need to know. I will challenge him to a fight. Claudio must pay for what he has done. Look after your cousin. I must tell everyone that she is dead. Goodbye.

[Exit Beatrice one way and Benedick the other]

Act 4, Scene 2

[Enter Dogberry, Verges, the sexton[63] and the Watch. Borachio and Conrad are their prisoners]

Dogberry: Is everyone here?

Verges: Yes, sir and ready to question these men too.

Dogberry: The prisoners must say their names *[To Borachio]* You first, friend.

Borachio: My name's Borachio.

Dogberry: Write that down, Neighbour Oatcake. Now, the other one.

Conrad: I am a gentleman. My name is Conrad.

Dogberry: A gentleman and a villain. Well, well. What do you say about that?

Conrad: I tell you that we are not villains.

Dogberry: That's very clear, but clearly you are false – both of you.

Borachio: No, that is false.

Dogberry: We agree then. Good. Write down all is false, Neighbour Oatcake.

Sexton: First you must speak to the Watch. Ask them what was said.

Dogberry: Of course, that comes next. Master Watchman, say what you heard.

1st Watchman: I heard this man say that Don John, the prince's brother, was a villain.

Dogberry: Write that down: The prince's brother is a villain. Well, that is terrible. Anything else?

Borachio: Sir, I must …

Dogberry: You must be quiet when the Watch is speaking.

2nd Watchman: I heard this man say that Don John had given him one thousand ducats.

Dogberry: One thousand ducats? What for?

2nd Watchman: For saying that Lady Hero was false!

Verges: That is really terrible. Did he say anything more?

1ˢᵗ Watchman: That Count Claudio would shame Hero in front of everyone and not marry her!

Dogberry: Oh, that is a shame indeed!

Sexton: But it happened exactly as Don John had planned. Our Lady Hero *was* shamed and later died. Don John himself left Messina in secret this morning. You must take these men to Don Pedro. I'll go to Leonato now with this news.

[Exit sexton]

Dogberry: *[To Borachio and Conrad]* You must face our prince. Come with us!

Conrad: Let go of me, you old fool! I am a gentleman!

Dogberry: Old fool! He called me an old fool! Write that down, Neighbour Oatcake!

Conrad: An old fool and an ass[64]! That's what you are – an ass!

Dogberry: An ass! He called me an ass! Write that down too. It must not be forgotten that I am an ass. This man is the blackest villain in Messina! He called me an ass!

[Exit with Borachio and Conrad as prisoners of the Watch]

Act 5, Scene 1

[Enter Leonato and his brother, Antonio]
Antonio: If you go on mourning your daughter like this, you will soon be dead too.
Leonato: I do not want advice from you or any man
Who has not lost a child. A child he loved
As I have loved my sweetest daughter, Hero.
You tell me to stop crying, but that cannot be.
There's nothing you or anyone can say
To end my tears. You must be silent
And let me mourn, so that the whole world can
See and hear how much I miss my daughter.
Antonio: Men are like children when they cry so loud.
Leonato: And so they are. However clever men may be
If they have toothache, they will feel the pain.
Antonio: Let others feel the same pain too. Fight back
At those who caused your daughter's shame and death.
Leonato: Now that is good advice that I shall follow.
My sad heart says my child was wrongly shamed.
And this I'll tell to those who spoke against her:
Claudio, the prince and all the others in the church.
[Enter Don Pedro and Claudio]
Antonio: Here's Claudio and the prince. They're in a hurry.
Don Pedro: Good day, good day.
Claudio: Good day to both of you.
Leonato: Now, listen, both of you ...
Don Pedro: We are in a hurry, Leonato ...
Leonato: In a hurry, are you? There's no point in that now.
Don Pedro: Please do not argue with us, my good friend.
Antonio: If arguing could put things right, you should be careful.
Claudio: What do you mean? Who has done you wrong?
Leonato: Why, *you* have, sir. You are a liar.

[Claudio begins to pull out his sword]
Don't draw your sword. I'm not afraid of you.
Claudio: I did not mean to frighten you, old man.
I acted without thinking.
Leonato: Do not make jokes and laugh at me, young man.
I'm old, I know, but I am not a fool.
Claudio, I tell you to your face, you have so wronged
My innocent child and me, her father, too,
That I have sworn to take revenge on you.
I may be old, but I *will* challenge you.
Your awful lies have shamed my innocent child,
And like sharp daggers, they have killed her too.
Her body rests inside the family tomb
Where shame had never come until this time.
This is your doing, villain!

Leonato: *Know, Claudio, to thy head,*
Thou hast so wronged my innocent child and me
That I am forced to lay my reverence by,
And with grey hairs and bruise of many days,
Do challenge thee to trial of a man.

lay … by = put to one side
reverence = expected behaviour
bruise = weakness of old age
trial = fight

Claudio: Villain? I'm no villain!
Leonato: Oh, yes you are.
Don Pedro: That is not true, old man.
Leonato: It is the truth – I'll prove it with my sword,
Although the count's a young and skilful fighter.
Claudio: That is enough and I refuse to fight you.
Leonato: You can't be free of me like that.
You've killed my child.
But if you kill me, boy, you've killed a man!

Your awful lies have shamed my innocent child,
And like sharp daggers, they have killed her too.

Antonio: You will kill two of us, for I'll fight too.
Come on, boy, come, I'll fight you now.
However good you are, I can do better.
And, as I am a gentleman, I will!
Leonato: Brother …
Antonio: God knows I loved my niece and she is dead.
Yes, shamed to death by villains, who I will kill
As I would kill a snake. They are like animals …
Leonato: Brother Antony …
Antonio: Let me speak, brother! They are useless, all of them.
With mocking, scornful tongues they hurt the weak
And dare not fight the strong.
Leonato: But Brother Antony …
Antonio: Don't worry, brother, I will take care of this.
Don Pedro: Gentlemen, please, we don't want to upset you.
I'm sorry that your daughter's dead, but you must know
Her shame was proved – there is no doubt of that.
Leonato: My lord, my lord …
Don Pedro: I will not listen to you.
[Enter Benedick]
Leonato: No? Then we'll find someone else who will.
Antonio: Yes, I agree. Or there will be trouble.
[Exit Leonato and Antonio]
Don Pedro: Here comes the man we both were looking for.
Claudio: What's your news, Signor Benedick?
Benedick: Good day, my lord.
Don Pedro: You are welcome, sir. There's nearly been a fight here!
Claudio: It was just two, toothless, old men trying hard to bite off our noses!
Don Pedro: Your friend means Leonato and his brother. If we had fought, we would have been too young for them!
Benedick: There is nothing brave in fighting for the wrong reason. I have come to find both of you.

Claudio: We have been looking for you too. We are feeling sad and need to be cheered up by your wit. Where has it gone?

Benedick: It's here, beside my sword. Shall I get it out?

Don Pedro: Is that where you keep your wit? At your side?

Claudio: A man beside his wit, is mad, out of his mind, isn't he? So pull out your wit. Let's see it!

Don Pedro: Wait a minute, something's the matter. What is it, Benedick? Are you sick? Or angry?

Claudio: Cheer up, Benedick! I've never seen you looking so sad!

Benedick: If you try to match your wit with mine, I'll win. I've had enough of this talk.

Claudio: Oh dear, you really do want a fight.

Don Pedro: This is not the Benedick we know! I think he's really angry.

Claudio: If he is, that's his problem.

Benedick: I have something to say to you, Count.

Claudio: *[Laughing]* Surely it's not a challenge!

Benedick: *[Quietly, to Claudio]* You are a villain. I am not joking now. Yes, I dare to challenge you. You must dare to fight or I shall dare to say you are afraid. You have killed a sweet lady and that's a terrible thing. You must give me your answer.

Claudio: Well, I agree, if it will keep you happy.

Don Pedro: What's going on? Something good, I hope. Are you planning a fine meal for us all?

Claudio: Well, a silly chicken, for sure, and a dumb calf's[65] head. And maybe tongue too? Anything I can cut up easily.

Benedick: Let's hope your dagger is sharper than your wit.

Don Pedro: Beatrice praised *your* wit the other day, Benedick. She agreed with me that you had a fine one. 'A fine little one,' was what she said. 'No, a big one,' I replied. 'All right then,' Beatrice answered, 'a great big heavy one.' 'Yes, but his wit is not hurtful. It is wise,' I answered, 'and this wise gentleman can speak other languages too.' Then the lady replied, 'Oh, yes, Benedick has so many different ways of saying things that his meaning is never clear'. Beatrice went on talking about you and your faults, for more than an hour. But in the end, she said that you were the finest man in Italy!

Claudio: Then the lady cried and said that it did not matter at all.

Don Pedro: That's true, but I am very sure that if she did not hate him, she would love him. Old Leonato's daughter told us all about Lady Beatrice's feelings.

Claudio: Yes, and our friend Benedick overheard[66] everything!

Don Pedro: So when do we put the horns on our wise friend's head?

Claudio: And make a sign that says: 'Here lives Benedick, the married man'. [Don Pedro and Claudio laugh at Benedick]

Benedick: Goodbye, boy. You know how I feel. I have had enough of your silly jokes, which have not hurt me at all. My thanks to you, Don Pedro, but I cannot be your friend a moment longer. Your brother, Don John, has left Messina in a hurry. All of you have caused the death of a sweet innocent lady. I have already challenged that boy there. I'll leave him in peace until we meet to fight.

[Exit Benedick]

Benedick: *Fare you well, boy, you know my mind. I will leave you now to your gossip-like humour. You break jests as braggarts do their blades, which God be thanked, hurt not. My lord, for your many courtesies I thank you. I must discontinue your company.*

gossip-like humour = foolish words
jests = jokes
braggarts = overconfident young men
blades = swords
courtesies = kind actions
discontinue = leave

Don Pedro: He is not joking now.

Claudio: I agree. It's all because of his love for Beatrice.

Don Pedro: He has challenged you.

Claudio: That's right, he has.

Don Pedro: How a man changes when he stops thinking for himself!

[Enter Dogberry, Verges and the Watch, with Conrad and Borachio]

Claudio: Yes, he has lost his wits. A fool may think him clever, but the witless man would look at the fool and think *him* even more clever!

Don Pedro: Wait a minute though. Benedick said that my brother had left Messina. That is worrying news.

Dogberry: *[To Borachio]* Come along, now, sir. You will have justice[67] if there is any in Messina, even though you are a liar.

Don Pedro: What's all this? Two of my brother's men made prisoners? And Borachio is one of them!

Claudio: Ask what they have done, my lord.

Don Pedro: Officers, why are these men your prisoners?

Dogberry: Well, sir, firstly, they have told lies and secondly, sworn those lies were true. Fourthly, they have said bad things about a good lady – bad things that are not true. Sixthly and lastly, they are both bad men, sir, very bad indeed. Everything they say is lies.

Don Pedro: *[Laughing]* First, I ask you what these men have done. Then I ask you why they are your prisoners and sixth and last, why you have brought them here to me.

Claudio: *[Laughing]* Well done, sir. You've put it very clearly. We'll soon have the truth now.

Don Pedro: I'll have to ask the prisoners themselves. This officer's words are too clever for me to understand. So, you two prisoners, tell me what you have done.

Borachio: Sweet prince, this is no laughing matter. Listen to me and then the count may kill me. These old men are fools, but they have found out what you did not. They heard me tell this man, Conrad, what I had done. It was your brother's idea, to shame poor Hero. You watched as Margaret, dressed as Hero, listened to my words of love. Later, the count shamed Hero in the church. These old men have the details. I am too ashamed to give them all again. The lady is dead, killed by my master's words and by mine too.

Don Pedro: *[To Claudio]* These words must be like a dagger in your heart.

Claudio: I am poisoned by his words.

Don Pedro: *[To Borachio]* Did my brother really tell you to do this?

Borachio: Yes, and he paid me well for doing it.

Don Pedro: My brother is a villain, that is true.
And now he's run away from his own villainy.

Claudio: Sweet Hero! Now I see you, pure and innocent,
The perfect girl whom I had seen at first.

Dogberry: Let's take the prisoners away. By now, the sexton will have told Signor Leonato everything.

Verges: Here comes Signor Leonato and the sexton too.
[Enter Leonato, Antonio and the sexton]

Leonato: Where is the villain? Let me look into his eyes.
Then, when I see another man like him,
I can be sure that he's a villain too.
Where is he?

Borachio: I am the man who's wronged you.

Leonato: Are you the man who killed my innocent child?

Borachio: Yes, it was me alone.

Leonato: That's not the truth, you villain.
These two men and a third who's gone
All played a part in it.
I thank you, princes, for my daughter's death.
What a fine thing it was to kill her!
You never should forget what you have done!

Claudio: I don't know if you'll listen, but I must speak.
Revenge is yours. Do what you like with me.

I have wronged your daughter and have wronged you too,
But by mistake and not by villainy.
Don Pedro: I can say the same.
But the revenge of this good old man
Must fall on my head too and I am ready.
Leonato: You cannot bring my daughter back to life –
That is impossible.
But let the people of Messina know that she was innocent.
Write a sad song, about her worthy life
Then put it on her tomb. Sing it aloud tonight.
And in the morning, come here to my house.
My brother has a child who looks exactly like
My dear, dead Hero. Marry this girl.
She is my brother's heir and my heir too.
You'll be my nephew, not my son-in-law
And my revenge will be forgotten.
Claudio: Oh, worthy sir, you are too good to me.
I do accept your offer and from now on,
I will do anything you ask of me.
Leonato: I shall expect you then, tomorrow. Now I am going.
This villain here will face Margaret tomorrow.
I believe she played a part in this and is to blame
Although she was following Don John's plan.
Borachio: No, that's not true, I swear. She did not understand
What she was doing and should not be blamed.
Dogberry: *[Pointing to Conrad]* Leonato, sir, please remember
that this villain here called me an ass, in front of all the Watch.
That must be written down, sir, and not forgotten.
Leonato: I thank you for the trouble you have taken. *[Gives
him money]*
Dogberry: God save you, sir! It was no trouble at all, sir.
Leonato: Go now, and leave your prisoners with me.
Dogberry: I leave them in good hands, sir. And I leave you
in good health! May you never forget that this villain called

me an ass. Please remember that, sir, when we meet again tomorrow. *I am an ass.* Make sure that it is written down, sir.
[Exit Dogberry and Verges]
Leonato: *[To Claudio and Don Pedro]*
Lords, I'll say goodbye to you too.
Antonio: Goodbye, my lords. We'll see you both tomorrow.
Don Pedro: We shall be there.
Claudio: Tonight I'll mourn at Hero's tomb.
Leonato: *[To the Watch]*
Keep your prisoners safe. We'll talk to Margaret and find out how she knew this man.
[All exit]

Act 5, Scene 2

[Enter Benedick, who meets Margaret]

Benedick: Mistress Margaret, please help me speak to Lady Beatrice.

Margaret: If I do, will you write a poem to my beauty?

Benedick: In the finest words possible, to describe your fine beauty!

Margaret: If it's as fine as that, why am I still unmarried?

Benedick: You are quick with your answers! Your wit's too sharp!

Margaret: As yours used to be, but it isn't now.

Benedick: Well, I don't want to use it on a woman, that's the truth. Words can be dangerous, especially for a woman. Do call Beatrice, so that I can speak to her.

Margaret: She has legs to bring her here. I expect she will come.

[Exit Margaret]

Benedick: I am sure she will. Let's see if I can finish my poem:
Who sits above
And knows me and knows
How sad love makes me ...

Love makes me sad, because I can't find the words to describe it. Many other men have written fine poems about love, why can't I? Love has turned me upside down, but I can't find a thing to say. I can't find words with the right sounds and sense: *lady* and *baby*, *scorn* and *horn*, *fool* and *school*? No, nothing's right. Oh dear.

[Enter Beatrice]

Sweet Beatrice! So you came when I asked you!

Beatrice: Yes, sir, and I'll go when you tell me to.

Benedick: Oh, stay until then!

Beatrice: 'Then' has been said, so goodbye! But before I go, I must know what happened between you and Claudio. That's why I came.

Benedick: Only bad words. We argued, that's all. Now I must kiss you.

Beatrice: From bad words straight to kisses? I don't think so.

Benedick: You are too sharp for me, lady. Now listen. I have challenged Claudio and I am waiting for his answer. And now I want to ask you something too. Which of my bad parts first made you fall in love with me?

Beatrice: Well, all of them at once. You have so many faults. But now, please tell me this. What was it about me that gave you the first pain of love?

Benedick: The first pain of love? You are right. Love is a pain – I love you because I can't stop myself, not because I want to.

Beatrice: Your heart is giving you good advice but, because of me, you don't listen to it. And I will do the same. Do both of us hate to love or love to hate? I only know one answer to that. When you love, I must love, although I hate to. Oh dear, we shall never agree on anything.

Benedick: That's right. We're so clever that we show our love by arguing.

Beatrice: Are you praising yourself?

Benedick: If a man doesn't praise himself, no one will. Unless he builds his own tomb, he will soon be forgotten.

Beatrice: And how soon is that?

Benedick: As soon as the death-bell stops ringing and his friends stop crying. So a wise man like me, must praise himself while he is alive. But please tell me how your cousin is doing.

Beatrice: Very badly.

Benedick: And you?

Beatrice: Very badly too.

[Enter Ursula]

Benedick: Pray to God, love me and things will get better. I will go now. Someone needs to speak to you, I think.

Ursula: Madam, you must come to your uncle at once. There's such a lot going on at home: it has been proved that my Lady

Hero was wrongly accused[68]. The prince and Claudio have also been wronged and Don John, who is to blame for all of this, has left Messina. Please come, madam.

Beatrice: Will you come and hear this news, sir?

Benedick: I will live in your heart, die in your arms and be buried in your eyes. And I will go with you to your uncle's house.

[All exit]

Act 5, Scene 3

[Enter Claudio, Don Pedro, Balthasar, servants and musicians]
Claudio: Is this Leonato's family tomb?
Servant: It is, sir.
Claudio: *[Reading]* 'Killed by men with wicked[69] tongues
Was the virgin who here lies.
In death, we try to right her wrongs
And give her praise that never dies.
So the life that died of shame
Takes again a worthy name.'
I hang this poem on her tomb,
Praising her when I have gone.
[To Balthasar] Now, play your music, sing your mourning song.
Balthasar: *[Singing]* Diana, goddess of the night
Forgive the men who caused the death
Of your sweet Hero. Hear their cries
As round her tomb they walk with many sighs[70].
Night is your time and at this time they mourn
And think of death that comes to all those born.
Sadly, sadly sing this song
And we will praise you all night long.
Claudio: Now, my sweetest girl, goodnight and for my wrongs
Year after year will I sing these mourning songs.
Don Pedro: Dawn's[71] fair first light is shining in the sky
So thanks to all – now we must say goodbye.
Claudio: Goodbye my friends. Now it is time to leave.
Don Pedro: Then let us go to Leonato's house. But first, we'll
change our mourning clothes. We must dress for a wedding.
Claudio: Then let this wedding day be happy.
We must forget the sadness of the past
And look ahead to future happiness.
[Exit]

Act 5, Scene 4

[Enter Leonato, Benedick, Beatrice, Margaret, Ursula, Antonio, Friar Francis and Hero]

Friar Francis: Did I not tell you that she was innocent?
Leonato: So are the prince and Claudio, who accused her
Because of a mistake that now has been explained.
But Margaret must be partly blamed for that,
Although she did not understand what she was doing –
That was made quite clear when she was questioned.
Antonio: Well, I am glad that now we know the truth.
Benedick: And so am I because I had promised Beatrice
That I would fight Count Claudio for his part in this.
Leonato: Well, daughter, you and all these ladies now must go
Into another room and wait there quietly
And when I send for you, come back wearing masks.
The prince and Claudio are on their way here too.
Brother Antonio, you have a part to play in this.
You must be father to your brother's daughter
And give my Hero to young Claudio.
[Exit ladies]
Antonio: I shall play that part with happiness.
Benedick: Friar, I must ask you to help me.
Friar Francis: What must I do for you, sir?
Benedick: To make me a married man – perhaps to ruin me!
The truth, Signor Leonato, is that your niece, Beatrice,
Has shown that she fancies me – she's in love.
Leonato: My daughter would agree with you, I think.
Benedick: And I love Beatrice, just as she loves me.
Leonato: All your friends have noticed that.
Benedick: I have decided that I want to marry Beatrice. She is your niece, I need you to agree. And if you do, this friar can marry us today.
Leonato: I agree with all my heart.

Friar Francis: And I am here to help you.
[Enter Don Pedro and Claudio]
Don Pedro: Good morning to you all.
Leonato: Good morning, Prince. Good morning, Claudio.
We are here for you. Do you still agree, Count Claudio,
To be married here to my brother's daughter?
Claudio: I do. I have not changed my mind.
Leonato: Then bring her here, Antonio. The friar is ready.
[Exit Antonio]
Don Pedro: Good morning, Benedick. What on earth's the matter? You look as grey and cloudy as a winter's day.
Claudio: He's thinking about horns – he always is – and how the great god, Jove, became a bull, to court the fair Europa. Now Benedick's in love and all of Europe will give him golden horns, just like a god.
Benedick: Perhaps your father was a bull too, sir, and you're a calf. Your silly bleating[72] makes you sound like one!
[Enter Antonio, Hero, Beatrice, Margaret and Ursula. The ladies are all wearing masks]
Claudio: I'll get my revenge for those words later. Now I have something else to do. Who is the lady I must make my wife?
Antonio: Here she is. I now give her to you.
Claudio: Then she is mine. Sweet, let me see your face.
Leonato: Not yet. First, you must take her hand and swear
To this good friar, that you will marry her.
Claudio: Give me your hand so that this friar can see.
If you will agree, I am your husband.
Hero: And when I lived, I was your other wife:
And when you loved, you were my other husband.
[Hero takes off her mask]
Claudio: Another Hero!
Hero: That is the truth.
One Hero died of shame, but I'm alive.
And just as I'm alive, I am a virgin.

Don Pedro: You are Leonato's Hero – the Hero who is dead!

Leonato: She lived again as soon as her shame died.

Friar Francis: I'll make that clear, but first they must be married. Then I'll tell everyone how Hero 'died' and came to life. But that can wait. To the church now, everyone!

Benedick: Wait a minute, friar. Which one of these ladies is Beatrice?

Beatrice: That is my name. What do you want of me?

[Beatrice takes off her mask]

Benedick: It is true that you love me, isn't it?

Beatrice: Love you? No, that's not the word I'd use.
I like you, I suppose. That's all.

Benedick: So then your uncle, the prince and Claudio have all got it wrong. They swore you loved me.

Beatrice: But it's true, isn't it, that you love me?

Benedick: Not more than I have to.

Beatrice: So then my cousin, Hero, Margaret and Ursula made a mistake. They swore you loved me too.

Benedick: They told me that love was making you ill.

Beatrice: They told me that your love was killing you.

Benedick: It doesn't matter. Then you really don't love me?

Beatrice: Not really. We are only friends.

Leonato: Come on, niece, I'm sure you love this gentleman.

Claudio: I am sure that he loves *her* and I'll tell you why.
Look at this paper. That is Benedick's writing.

[Claudio shows everyone a sheet of paper]

Yes, it's a poem, quite a bad one too, in praise of Lady Beatrice.

Hero: *[Showing another sheet of paper]* And here's a letter, taken from my cousin's pocket. It's in her writing and guess what it's about – her love, of course, for Signor Benedick.

Benedick: This is a great surprise! I can't believe it. Our hands are saying that our hearts are lying. Come, you can be mine, but only because I feel sorry for you.

Beatrice: Well, I won't say no because my friends have told

87

me again and again that I should say yes. Also, I will say yes partly to save your life – I have been told that you are very ill.
Leonato: Now that's enough. Kiss her, Benedick! It's the only way to stop the lady talking!
[Benedick and Beatrice kiss]
Don Pedro: How are you now, Benedick, the 'married man'?
Benedick: I'll tell you what, prince, not even a crowd of jokers could make me change my mind. I have decided to marry and that's the end of it. Forget all the bad things I have said about marriage – I have changed my mind for the very last time. And Claudio, I had planned to fight you, but now you will be family. So now you don't need to be scared to love my cousin, Hero.
Claudio: If you had said no to Beatrice, I would have made you find someone else to be unfaithful to. Of course, I'm sure you would be unfaithful. My cousin, Beatrice, will have to keep an eye on you P.

Claudio: *I had well hoped that thou wouldst have denied Beatrice, that I might have cudgelled thee out of thy single life to make thee a double-dealer, which out of question thou wilt be, if my cousin do not look exceedingly narrowly to thee.*

thou = you
cudgelled = beaten
double-dealer = dishonest husband
exceedingly = very
narrowly = carefully

Benedick: Come, Claudio, don't talk like that. We are friends, you know. Let's all have one last dance together, before we get married. In that way, we can make our own hearts lighter and our ladies ready for love.
Leonato: We'll have the dancing after the weddings.
Benedick: No, before! Start playing, you musicians! Prince, you are a sad man. You should get married yourself. No man's ever too old for that.

Kiss her, Benedick! It's the only way to stop the lady talking!

[Enter a messenger]
Messenger: My lord, your brother John has been caught trying to escape. Your soldiers are bringing him back to Messina.
Benedick: We'll think about him tomorrow – and what to do to him. Musicians, play!
[All exit, dancing]

Points for Understanding

Act 1

1 The messenger brought good news to Messina. What was it?
2 What did Beatrice and Benedick always do when they met?
3 What did Benedick think about marriage?
4 Claudio wanted to marry Hero. How did Don Pedro plan to help him?
5 What kind of man was Don John?
6 Why did Don John want to stop Claudio marrying Hero?

Act 2

1 Why did Beatrice not want a husband?
2 While they were dancing and everyone was wearing a mask, both Benedick and Claudio heard bad news. What exactly did they hear?
3 What did each of the two men then want to do?
4 Don Pedro soon made Claudio happy again. How did he do that?
5 Don Pedro had a plan to make the time pass quickly. What was the plan and who agreed to help him?

Act 3

1 Borachio, Don John's friend, had a plan to stop the marriage. What was it?
2 Why did Borachio think his plan would succeed?
3 Benedick overheard his friends talking about Beatrice. What did they say she had said and done?
4 Why did Benedick believe what he had overheard? What did he decide to do next?
5 How did Beatrice feel after she had overheard her cousin and servants talking about her?
6 Benedick's friends saw some changes in him. What were these changes and what did they mean?

7 Don John told Claudio that Hero was unfaithful. Why do you think that Claudio believed him?
8 Why did the Watch take Borachio and Conrad to prison?
9 Hero was getting ready for her wedding. How did she feel? How did Beatrice and Margaret feel?

Act 4

1 Claudio accused Hero of being unfaithful. Who believed that was true? Who did not believe it? What did Hero do?
2 Friar Francis had a plan. What was it?
3 What did Beatrice ask Benedick to do? Did he agree or not?
4 How was the truth about Hero made clear?

Act 5

1 Antonio had two pieces of advice for his brother, Leonato. What were they?
2 Who told everyone the truth about Don John's plan to shame Hero?
3 Leonato told Claudio to do two things. What were they?
4 Beatrice and Benedick found out that they had both been tricked. What did they do next?
5 The play ended happily. What was going to happen?

Glossary

1 **retired** – *to retire* (page 5)
to stop working, especially when you reach the age when you are officially too old to work

2 **governor** (page 6)
an official whose job is to control and manage an area, city, or country and its people

3 **witty** (page 6)
clever and funny

4 **villain** (page 7)
the main bad character in a story, play, film etc. The main good character is the *hero* or *heroine*.

5 **bastard** (page 7)
used to describe someone whose parents are not married to each other. This word is now considered to be offensive.

6 **count** (page 9)
a man who is a member of the highest social class in some European countries, but not in the UK. *Count* is also used as a title before the man's name.

7 **victory** (page 10)
the fact of winning a competition or battle, or an occasion when someone wins

8 **praises** – *to praise someone or something* (page 10)
to express strong approval or admiration for someone or something, especially in public. An expression of strong approval or admiration is called *praise*.

9 **Signor Sharp-sword** (page 10)
a *sword* is a weapon with a short handle and a long blade which is *sharp* – a *sharp* object has an edge that can cut or an end that is pointed. Beatrice is making a joke about Benedick's name.

10 **challenged** – *to challenge someone to something* (page 10)
to invite someone to compete or fight. An invitation to someone to compete or fight is called a *challenge*.

11 **fool** (page 10)
a man in the past whose job was to entertain a king, queen, or other important person by making them laugh. Nowadays, a *fool* is someone who does not behave in an intelligent or sensible way. Beatrice uses this word in both of its meanings. Someone who is

lacking good sense and judgment is described as *foolish*. If you trick someone by making them believe something that is not true, you *fool* them.

12 **arrow** (page 10)

a weapon in the form of a thin straight stick with a sharp point at one end and feathers at the other

13 **merry** (page 11)

happy and lively

14 **wits** (page 11)

Shakespeare often wrote in his plays about the five *wits* – these were common sense, imagination, fantasy or humour, the ability to form good judgements, and memory. Generally, the word is used to mean *intelligence*. Beatrice and Benedick enjoy a *challenge of wits* – a competition to see who can be the most clever, imaginative and funny.

15 **devil** (page 11)

the most powerful evil spirit in many religions such as Christianity, Judaism, and Islam

16 **noble** (page 11)

belonging to the highest social class

17 **scorn** (page 12)

a feeling that someone or something is not good enough to deserve your approval or respect. If you *scorn* someone or something, you treat them as if they do not deserve your approval or respect. This behaviour is described as *scornful*. Benedick is saying that Beatrice is full of *scorn*.

18 **scratched** (page 12)

cut with something sharp, such as your finger nails

19 **parrot** (page 12)

a brightly coloured tropical bird that is often kept as a pet and can be taught to say a few words

20 **dumb** (page 12)

on old-fashioned word meaning permanently unable to speak. This word is now more commonly used to mean *stupid* and is offensive. Claudio uses *dumb* with this meaning in Act 5.

21 **worthy** (page 14)

a worthy person or thing has qualities that make people respect them. If someone is *worthy of* something, such as love or admiration, they deserve it. Something's *worth* is how good, useful, or important it is. You say that something *is worth something* or *worth doing*.

22 **mock** – *to mock someone or something* (page 14)
to make someone or something look stupid by laughing at them,
copying them, or saying something that is not kind

23 **fair** (page 14)
someone who is *fair* has light hair and pale skin, but Hero's hair is
brown. Another meaning of *fair* is *beautiful*. Benedick is using both
meanings to make a joke. He says that her hair is too dark to call
her beautiful. In Act 2, Beatrice also uses the word *fair*, but in its
most common meaning – reasonable and morally right.

24 **fancy** – *to fancy someone* (page 14)
to feel sexually attracted to someone

25 **unfaithful** (page 15)
having a sexual relationship with someone who is not your
husband, wife, or partner

26 **bachelor** (page 15)
a man who has never been married

27 **horns** (page 16)
the hard pointed parts that usually grow in a pair on the heads
of some animals, for example cows or goats. Traditionally, a man
whose wife has a sexual relationship with another man is said to
wear horns on his head. Benedick is saying that he will never marry
because he does not want to have a wife who is unfaithful to him.

28 **target** (page 16)
an object that you have to hit in a game or a sport

29 **heir** (page 16)
someone who will receive money, property, or a title when another
person dies

30 **mask** (page 17)
something that you wear to cover part or all of your face in order to
hide who you are or for decoration

31 **disguise** – *to disguise someone* (page 17)
to make changes in the way that someone looks so that other
people will not recognize them

32 **servant** (page 18)
someone whose job is to live and travel with someone of a higher
social class in order to serve them and look after them

33 **thorn** (page 19)
a sharp point that sticks out from the stem of a plant

34 **muzzle** (page 19)
something that you put around the nose and mouth of a dog to
prevent it from biting people

35 **ruin** – *to ruin something* (page 19)
to destroy or severely damage something

36 **pretend** – *to pretend to be someone or something* (page 20)
to behave in a particular way because you want someone to believe
that something is true when it is not

37 **court** – *to court someone* (page 20)
to try to impress or please someone because you want to have a
romantic relationship with them

38 **revenge** (page 20)
something that you do to hurt or punish someone because they
have hurt you or someone else

39 **poison** – *to poison something* (page 20)
to put a substance which can kill you or make you ill into food or
drink because you want to harm someone

40 **gentlewoman** (page 21)
a woman from a high social class who lives and travels with another
woman with a higher position in society in order to help her and
look after her

41 **rough** (page 21)
with a surface that is not smooth

42 **virgin** (page 22)
someone who has never had sex, especially a girl or young woman

43 **earth** (page 22)
the substance in which plants grow that covers most of the land

44 **mourn** – *to mourn (for) something* (page 27)
to be sad or disappointed because something no longer exists or is
not as good as it was in the past

45 **nest** (page 27)
a structure that birds make to keep their eggs and babies in

46 **insulted** – *to insult someone* (page 27)
to say or do something offensive

47 **dagger** (page 28)
a weapon like a very small sword

48 **trick** – *to trick someone into doing something* (page 32)
to influence someone in a clever or dishonest way, so that they do
something you want them to do

49 **proof** (page 33)
information or evidence that shows that something is definitely
true or definitely exists

50 **note** – *to note something* (page 36)
to notice or realize something. Another meaning of this verb is to mention something. A *note* is also an individual sound in music. Balthasar uses all three meanings of *note* in this sentence. He is cleverly saying that Don Pedro should realize that his music is not good enough to be mentioned.

51 **blamed** – *to blame someone* (page 40)
to say or think that someone or something is responsible for an accident, problem, or bad situation

52 **headdress** (page 44)
something that someone wears on their head as a decoration, especially when they are getting married, with jewels like a small crown and artificial hair

53 **perfume** (page 45)
a liquid with a pleasant smell that you put on your skin

54 **the Watch** (page 50)
a group of people whose job is to guard something. These people are called *watchmen*.

55 **lantern** (page 50)
a light inside a glass container with a handle for carrying it in your hand or on a long stick

56 **pearl** (page 54)
a small round jewel that is white and shiny and that grows inside the shell of a sea creature called an oyster

57 **sleeve** (page 54)
the part of a piece of clothing that covers your arm

58 **regret** – *to regret something* (page 60)
to feel sorry or sad about something that you have said or done

59 **faints** – *to faint* (page 62)
to suddenly become unconscious for a short time, and usually fall to the ground

60 **ink** (page 64)
a black or coloured liquid used for writing, drawing, or printing

61 **tomb** (page 65)
a large stone structure above the ground that contains a dead body

62 **swear** – *to swear* (page 66)
to make a sincere statement that you are telling the truth

63 **sexton** (page 69)
someone whose job is to look after a church and the buildings connected with it

64 **ass** (page 70)
a grey or brown animal similar to a horse, but smaller and with long ears. *Asses* are traditionally considered to be stupid.

65 **calf** (page 75)
a young cow

66 **overheard** – *to overhear something* (page 76)
to hear what people are saying during a conversation that you are not involved in

67 **justice** (page 77)
a fair result or punishment

68 **accused** – *to accuse someone* (page 83)
to say that someone has done something wrong or committed a crime

69 **wicked** (page 84)
morally wrong and deliberately intending to hurt people

70 **sigh** (page 84)
a slow breath out that makes a long soft sound, especially because you are sad, tired, annoyed, or relaxed

71 **dawn** (page 84)
the beginning of the day, when it begins to get light

72 **bleating** (page 86)
the sound that a young animal such as a sheep or calf makes

Useful Phrases

on my side – *to be on someone's side* (page 20)
if you are on someone's side, you support them in an argument or a fight

I'll make the most of it – *to make the most of something* (page 24)
if you *make the most of something*, you get the best possible advantage from it

I'll do my best – *to do your best* (page 36)
to try as hard as you can in order to achieve something

it is all up to me – *to be up to someone* (page 40)
if something is up to you, you are the person who makes a decision about it

I have made up my mind – *to make up your mind* (page 40)
to make a decision

My ears are burning – *somebody's ears are burning* (page 44)
if you say that somebody's ears are burning, you mean that other people are talking about them

he's short of money – *to be short of something* (page 45)
to have used almost all of a particular thing so that there is not much left

That settles it (page 45)
used for saying that you have made a decision because you have enough information, or because you do not want an annoying or unpleasant situation to continue

Shame on you! (page 54)
used for telling someone that they should feel guilty or embarrassed

Beatrice will have to keep an eye on you – *to keep an eye on someone* (page 88)
to watch someone carefully, especially because you do not trust them

Glossary and Useful Phrases definitions adapted from Macmillan English Dictionary 2nd Edition
© *Macmillan Publishers Limited 2007* www.macmillandictionaries.com

Exercises

Background Information

Give short answers to the questions.

1 Where was William Shakespeare born? _____Stratford-upon-Avon_____

2 What did John Shakespeare do? _____

3 How old was William Shakespeare when he got married? _____

4 How many children did he have? _____

5 What was his first job in London? _____

6 What company did he work for? _____

7 Where did the company perform? _____

8 Who was the Queen of England at this time? _____

9 How many people lived in London then? _____

10 How many theatres were there in London? _____

11 Which people had seats in theatres? _____

12 What time did the plays start? _____

13 When did Shakespeare stop writing plays? _____

14 When did he die? _____

15 Where is the new Globe Theatre? _____

About the Play

Choose the correct information to complete the sentences.

1 *Much Ado About Nothing* was first performed towards the beginning / (end) of 1598.

2 The play is a comedy / tragedy.

3 It is set in Spain / Sicily.

4 The city of Messina was governed by Italy / Spain.

5 It is / is not an original story.

6 There are two / three stories in the play.

7 The story of Beatrice and Benedick is always remembered / forgotten.

8 Will Kemp played evil / comedy characters.

9 Blank verse makes stories slower / faster.

10 The title has two / three meanings.

People in the Story

Complete the gaps. You can use some names more than once.

Antonio Beatrice Benedick Borachio ~~Claudio~~
Dogberry Don John Don Pedro Hero Leonato

1 Hero was in love with _____ *Claudio* _____ .

2 Leonato was _____'s father.

3 Don Pedro was related to _____ .

4 Beatrice had many arguments with _____ .

5 _____ found out the truth about Don John's plan.

6 _____ was the governor of Messina.

7 Beatrice was _____'s niece.

8 _____ came from Florence.

9 Benedick married _____ .

10 _____ was a Spanish prince.

11 _____ suggested a plan to ruin Hero.

12 _____ was Leonato's brother.

True or False?

Read the statements about *Much Ado About Nothing.*
Write True (T) or False (F).

1	Claudio didn't fall in love with Hero before he went to fight.	T
2	Beatrice and Benedick thought they hated each other.	
3	Beatrice and Benedick liked the idea of marriage.	
4	Beatrice and Benedick were clever and funny.	
5	Don Pedro wanted to marry Hero.	
6	Don John wanted to hurt Claudio.	
7	Don Pedro and Don John planned to make Beatrice and Benedick fall in love.	
8	Don John planned to stop Claudio from marrying.	
9	Benedick didn't believe what he overheard about Beatrice's love for him.	
10	The watchmen discovered Don John's plans.	
11	Claudio rejected Hero before the wedding.	
12	Hero died.	
13	Borachio told Don Pedro and Claudio about the lie.	
14	Claudio refused to marry another woman.	
15	Beatrice and Benedick agreed to marry.	
16	Don John was caught.	

Vocabulary: Anagrams

Write the letters in the correct order to make words which match the definitions.

1	GHIS	*sigh*	a slow breath out that makes a long, soft sound
2	TRANNLER		a light inside a glass container
3	ROPTAR		a brightly coloured tropical bird which can repeat words
4	GREENEV		something that you do to hurt someone because they have hurt you
5	HORNT		a sharp point on a rose, for example
6	KWIDEC		morally wrong and deliberately intending to hurt people
7	FALC		a young cow
8	SIONPO		to put a substance which can kill you into food or drink
9	GROUH		with a surface that is not smooth
10	THORWY		a person or cause that has good qualities

Vocabulary: Odd one out

Circle the word which is different.

1 (worthy)   dumb   rough   wicked

2 perfume   headdress   dawn   pearls

3 dagger   target   arrow   poison

4 fool   muzzle   heir   governor

5 calf   parrot   ass   horns

6 justice   victory   revenge   wits

Words from the Story

Complete the gaps. Use each word in the box once. You may need to change the form of the verbs.

> bachelor   faint   fancy   masks   merry   mourn
> revenge   ~~scorn~~   trick   unfaithful   villain   witty

1 Beatrice often ___*scorned*___ Benedick and did not respect him.

2 Don John was the main _____ in the story. He did some bad things.

3 Beatrice and Benedick were both very _____ . They were clever and funny.

4 Secretly, Benedick _____ Beatrice. He liked her very much.

5 Benedick never wanted to marry. He always wanted to be a _____ .

6 Beatrice was always happy and _____ .

7 At the dance, everyone wore _____ to hide their faces.

8 Benedick was upset by what Beatrice said about him at the dance. He wanted _____ .

9 Don John _____ Claudio into believing Margaret was Hero.

10 Claudio thought Hero had been _____ to him with other men.

11 Hero was so shocked that she _____ to the ground.

12 Leonato looked sad as he _____ the death of his daughter.

105

Useful Phrases

Match the two halves to make phrases from the story.

1 to be on	your best
2 to make the	your mind
3 to do	of something
4 to be	on you
5 to make up	up to you
6 your ears	your side
7 to be short	are burning
8 that	most of it
9 shame	eye on you
10 to keep an	settles it

Match the phrases above to the meanings below.

A   I haven't got the money I need. _7_

B   I get the best result I can from a bad situation. ....

C   It's the thing that helped me to decide. ....

D   Someone is talking about you. ....

E   I support you. ....

F   You should feel bad about what you said or did. ....

G   I always try as much as possible. ....

H   It's your decision. ....

I   I need to be careful of you. ....

J   Decide what you want. ....

Grammar: Verbs

Match the verbs with the definitions on the right.

1 to swear	to feel sorry about something that you have said or done
2 to blame someone	to make a sincere statement that you are telling the truth
3 to accuse someone	to make someone look stupid by laughing at them
4 to overhear something	to say or do something offensive
5 to regret something	to hear what people are saying in a conversation that you are not involved in
6 to insult someone	to say that someone is responsible for an accident, problem or bad situation
7 to mock someone	to say that someone has done something wrong

Now complete the gaps. Use each word above once.

1 Hero _____*swore*_____ she was innocent.

2 A servant .... Don Pedro saying that he loved Hero.

3 Leonato .... Claudio of lying about Hero.

4 Borachio .... tricking Claudio.

5 Beatrice .... Benedick at the dance and he felt bad.

6 Leonato .... Claudio for Hero's death.

7 Benedick often said things to .... women to make them look stupid.

Grammar: *Used to*

Rewrite the sentences using *used to* or *didn't use to*.

> **Example 1:** *Claudio didn't talk about love all the time.*
> Claudio didn't use to talk about love all the time.
> **Example 2:** *Claudio thought about war.*
> Claudio used to think about war.

1   Benedick didn't want get married.

_____

_____

2   Beatrice didn't believe in marriage.

_____

_____

3   Beatrice mocked Benedick.

_____

_____

4   Benedick didn't wear perfume.

_____

_____

5   Benedick had a beard.

_____

_____

6   Benedick worried about wearing horns.

_____

_____

Grammar: The third conditional

Rewite the sentences using the third conditional.

> Benedick heard his friends talking about Beatrice. He fell in love with her.
> *If Benedick hadn't heard his friends talking about Beatrice, he wouldn't have fallen in love with her.*

1   Claudio believed Don John. He didn't marry Hero.

_____

_____

2   The Watch overheard Borachio. Don John's plan didn't work.

_____

_____

3   Leonato didn't listen to Dogberry the first time. Hero was shamed.

_____

_____

4   Claudio discovered Don John's trick. He married Hero in the end.

_____

_____

5   Benedick challenged Claudio. Beatrice asked him to.

_____

_____

6   Borachio told Conrad about the trick. The Watch heard him.

_____

_____

Making Questions

Write questions for the answers given.

> **Example:** When *was Shakespeare born?*
> Shakespeare was born in 1564

Q1 What

A1 Beatrice called Benedick a fool.

Q2 Who

A2 Don John fought against Don Pedro in the war.

Q3 Where

A3 Borachio was in one of the rooms when he overheard Don Pedro and Claudio.

Q4 Who

A4 Beatrice was secretly in love with Benedick.

Q5 How long

A5 Borachio had known Margaret for at least a year.

Q6 What

A6 Don John told Claudio that Hero had been unfaithful to him.

Q7 Where

A7 The Watch overheard Borachio and Conrad in the street.

Q8 What

A8 Claudio decided to shame Hero.

Q9 What

A9 Hero fainted when she heard Claudio's words.

Q10 What

A10 Beatrice asked Benedick to kill Claudio.

Q11 What

A11 Conrad called Dogberry an ass.

Q12 Who

A12 Claudio promised to marry Leonato's niece.

Q13 Who

A13 Leonato's niece was really Hero.

Q14 How

A14 The story ended with a dance.

Published by Macmillan Heinemann ELT
Between Towns Road, Oxford OX4 3PP
A division of Macmillan Publishers Limited
Companies and representatives throughout the world
Heinemann is the registered trademark of Pearson Education, used under licence.

ISBN 978–0–2304–0859–3
ISBN 978–0–2304–0870–8 (with CD edition)

This version of *Much Ado About Nothing* by William Shakespeare was
retold by Margaret Tarner for Macmillan Readers.

First published 2011
Text © Macmillan Publishers Limited 2011
Design and illustration © Macmillan Publishers Limited 2011

Illustrated by Bruce Emmett
Cover photograph by Alistair Muir, Regent's Park Open Air Theatre, 2009

Printed and bound in Thailand

without CD edition

2016	2015	2014	2013	2012	2011
10	9	8	7	6	5	4	3	2	1

with CD edition

2016	2015	2014	2013	2012	2011
10	9	8	7	6	5	4	3	2	1